REQUIEM FOR TWELVE COWS

Author of *Twelve Cows—And We're In Clover*

Requiem
for
Twelve Cows

BY GEORGE REHM

WILLIAM MORROW AND COMPANY

NEW YORK

REQUIEM FOR TWELVE COWS

1.

A LONG, LONG TIME AGO, a good baker's dozen in years, I became owner of my first farm and my first cow. There were, in fact, eight cows that came with the place when I bought it. I had then a few vague notions about farms; as for cows, I knew absolutely nothing, had never even been close to one. I kept them because I discovered that northeastern Pennsylvania is primarily dairy country, that milk cows brought in a regular semimonthly cash income which struck me as well-nigh miraculous, and that, my ignorance being of monumental proportions, I might as well try dairying as any other means of livelihood on my 155 acres of woods and fields.

Not at all uniquely, I proposed to contribute a new page to that long, continuing story of the urbanite turned ruralite. I was fifty-three and wanted to be on my own, in open country, with fresh air to breathe, earth to walk on instead of pavements, the four seasons, rain and snow, heat and cold.

In return for my labors I asked only a modest living and tranquillity. Others had done it before me; I could do it also. I was but one of the many willing to exchange city amenities for rustic independence—one more reverter to the pioneer spirit.

Well, a lot of water has flowed over my dams since that great day in the early winter of 1947. A graph depicting my ups and downs, my nadirs of despair and my apogees of triumph, would rival the wildest roller-coaster in existence. The pace is even wilder. No sooner is a peak of serenity reached than it crumbles, collapses, and down I go into a wallow of mishaps and near disasters. I have learned to foresee and forestall some of them, but there is always a surprise to be sprung that catches me off guard and again I am flattened. But not yet counted out. On the contrary, when all debits and credits are added and balanced, the scale leans slightly to the plus side. By a thin margin, I admit, but a perceptible one. So I score the venture as a somewhat qualified success. After all, there is no denying I am still very much alive with nearly fourteen years of dairying chalked up. And I wouldn't have missed them for anything in the world.

Three years after I bought the farm and named it High Meadows, I wrote a book about my initiation into dairying. The title, *Twelve Cows and We're in Clover*, was slightly exaggerated. Our share of the clover, the financial side, was pretty thin. The cows were surer of a meal than we were. However, by my request, I was alone during the first winter and was prepared to accept a restricted diet if need be. All in all, I fared quite well. I was so busy learning the fundamentals of my new vocation and so worn out every evening from physical toil I was not accustomed to that a warmed-over stew tasted as good as a *cordon bleu* banquet. In particular I was getting acquainted with the cows and soon offering libations to the gods who had cast my lot with such animals. Bovine patience and imperturbability were welcome props throughout my neophyte stage. Sure, I got kicked occasionally, and they were frequently bored by my blunders and ineptness, but for the most part they took it all in stride and I looked on them with fond, forgiving eye. I still do. I doubt if any other animal would have condoned my clumsiness as they did.

There was a horse to bring round to friendly tolerance of my ignorance, a steady old mare who also was part and parcel of the farm. She did not fret unduly as I made repeated attempts to throw a harness over her back in such a way that at least a few of the innumerable buckles corresponded with appropriate straps. All too often I was more firmly snared in leather loops than was Molly. Once she was hitched to the wagon I could guide her with fair accuracy toward my target of the moment but I soon gave up hope of backing up through such narrow openings as the barn door. Molly's zeal to be helpful was more than I could control with the reins. Invariably she and the wagon wound up at a sharp right angle to each other, and the wagon whammed into the door frame.

Spring brought haying season—and my next big job. An antique mowing machine was among the pieces of machinery included in the price of the farm; and because it was too heavy for one horse to pull through thick grass, I launched a search for a working partner for Molly. To flatter myself that I knew the first thing about judging horseflesh was obviously preposterous. I didn't believe I could even bluff a farmer into thinking I knew such esoteric lore. So when I finally came upon a big, rangy animal, rather handsome in his way and certainly strong, I simply plunged—and bought him for sixty dollars. Doc (the name came with him and I never dared try to teach him a new one) was a gelding, with a rather low I.Q. and ideas of his own about work. However, he and Molly took to each other, and with a mixture of coaxing and cursing I got considerable work out of my team.

Farm machinery possessed secrets that I was some time in grasping. How was I to know that the whole section of cutting knives could be slipped from the cutter bar of the mowing machine for sharpening? I was deeply embarrassed, you can be sure, when a neighbor found me engaged, with no result, in filing the knives while still in place. To him such ignorance was beyond comprehension. Yet, being a good neighbor, he gave me a brief schooling in mower operation. He was also the one who gave me a severe scolding. That time he came across a field where I was cutting hay, and I climbed down to talk with him, stepping over and in front of the cutter bar. "Don't ever do that," he yelled at me. And then with considerable profanity he explained that should the horses be startled and jump ahead at such a moment, I could easily be hamstrung by the knives. I never did that again.

So it went. Always there was something new, almost unfathomable at first, then slowly straightening out to a series of simple movements, and as my efficiency increased, there were compensations along with the innumerable setbacks. I became absurdly proud when I succeeded in guiding the horses both at the appropriate gait and without veering so that the mower snick-snicked along the swath line and the tall grasses toppled back in ordered files and ranks. My spirits leaped when I could ride the mower seat as securely as an armchair, manipulating levers and pedals almost without thinking.

My wife Mary came out for the summer and Scoop, our

son, joined us when school was out. So we were three for the haying operation. I took over the mowing job. Scoop drove the dump rake like a racing sulky. Then we pitched hay onto the wagon with Mary steering the horses. And we loved it. We can still relive the ecstasy that filled us when we had completed a load of hay late in the afternoon and we would all get aboard for the ride to the barn. Sunk deep in the hay, breathing its sweetly pungent odor, we relaxed while gazing across miles of wooded ridges, the air beginning to freshen as the sun descended toward those ridges. Tired we were, dusty and sweaty, but brimming with a satisfaction so intense that we were in suspension, disembodied. Until Scoop, then seventeen, sang out that he was famished, as I was, and we drove happily to the barn, where I still had some cows to milk before dinner.

Much has changed since those first months. Work was made easier by better machinery, new equipment was added. I became more proficient at my various chores, milking was completed with diminishing strain, my affection for the cows rose to new heights and there were daily intervals of leisure. And always through the years there have been those moments of supreme satisfaction and well-being, short lived though they frequently were. Though the disappointments were greater than I could possibly have anticipated, the rewards approximated, often surpassed, those that had been imagined and that had urged me to try farming.

World War II was the disruptive factor that made it virtually impossible for me to return to confined work indoors. I have always had a weakness for picking up a hat and a toothbrush and heading for new horizons. I left college to volunteer as an ambulance driver in France with the American Field

Service in World War I. When the American Army took over much of the French front I was informed that, despite months of driving close to the lines, my glasses made me fit only for base-hospital work. With no intention of wielding a bedpan for the rest of the war, I signed up with the Red Cross and drove an ambulance on the Italian front for six months. That became so dull that I returned to France and volunteered for the French Foreign Legion. The examining officer there took one quick look at me, naked except for my glasses, saw all my members were intact and, without fussing over details, signed me up. I was ordered to the field artillery school at Fontainebleau for training, emerged as an *aspirant*, a subsecond lieutenant, and was sent to the front. The war soon ended, the regiment went to the Saar for the occupation, and early in 1919 word arrived that American volunteers in the Legion could be demobilized on request. Two American friends and I took immediate advantage of that, survived a chaotic celebration in Strasbourg and returned to Paris. Another celebration there, and we were on our way back to the United States.

Uncertain of what I wanted to do, other than that I did not care to return to college, I broke into newspaper work in my home town of Chicago at the munificent wage of $12 a week. Reporting struck me as the only gainful job that rhymed with my restlessness. It did, too, and after a year or so the pay envelope was up to $40. That was with the *Chicago Tribune*. Money, however, was not enough to settle me. The upshot was that when a friend, who also had been an ambulance driver in France, proposed that we return, I was more than willing. I sold my belongings, books and all, amassed a little more than enough cash for the cheapest passage and off we went. There were wartime friends still in Paris, and I also discovered that the *Tribune* had begun to publish a Paris edition, where I had a good chance for a job. The two of us counted our wealth, and decided we could afford a walking trip through southern France before subjecting ourselves once again to the confining atmosphere of a job. We headed south with a knapsack each and not much more. The all-important thing was that we were on the move.

A few weeks later we were in Marseilles, ever since one of my two favorite cities, always with the exception of Paris, Naples being the other. They are both brawling, noisy, dirty, extraordinarily human ports, full of color and a pervading don't-give-a-damn attitude that perfectly suited us. In Marseilles we heard that a private yacht, owned by an American, had arrived in harbor, on the first lap of a trip around the world with the owner and his bride. That inspired the great scheme that we should join the crew as journalistic deckhands, equally capable of polishing brasswork and handling occasional publicity. I am positive that only Ben Ali McAfee, late of Stamford, Connecticut, was screwball enough among yacht owners to accept such an utterly mad proposal, yet he did. And we sailed on the good ship *Xarifa*, with quarters in a big cabin aft where his car was housed when at sea. It was agreed that we would receive no pay, only board and living space. But we still had a little cash left, and we added a bit to it by teaching the first, second and third mates the fundamentals of poker, still more by a few lucky *coups* at the gambling casino at Nice. The entire crew, I should state, was British, formerly on Lord Beatty's yacht, happier with sail than steam, and a splendid lot from stoker Ernie, a kind of Neanderthal Cockney, to the captain, but especially the first mate, Morgan, a true English seaman of the old school. I still have a document signed by the skipper awarding me able-bodied seaman rating though I doubt it would ever be recognized as legal.

Worrisome reports from the New York Stock Exchange obliged McAfee to remain in the Mediterranean; so we went on from Nice to Genoa, to Naples, to Tunis, with long stops in each port. There he decided to abandon his world cruise and sail for England. That did not appeal to us, we discussed the matter with McAfee, he agreed he no longer had need of two journalist-deckhands, as if he had had at any time, and when we replied to his query that we were broke, he gave us a thousand franc note each. What a person! For years afterward, I met him occasionally in the Ritz bar in Paris, where he had installed his ex-cabin boy, André, as assistant bartender, and we would drink and laugh over that madcap affair.

Our trip did not end at Tunis, however. With money in our pockets, we traveled to Biskra, hoping we might join a caravan to Egypt, but border troubles with Libya ended that venture. We returned to Tunis and took a cattleboat to Malta with the idea of continuing our jaunt eastward on a cargo ship —after all, we had AB seaman's papers. But when we learned that no American ships were expected there in the near future, we took steerage passage on a small ship to Marseilles and thence reached Paris broke and very hungry. A few days later we had jobs, I with the *Tribune*, my friend with the Paris *Herald*.

All this has nothing to do with High Meadows, of course, but it is indicative of the footloose mood resulting from the war, carefree and confident that tomorrow would take care of itself. Which, oddly enough, it always did. With a newspaper job as a reliable stake in Paris, first on the *Tribune*, then the Paris *Times*, then the Paris *Herald*, I managed to interlard periods of work with prolonged trips—a bicycle tour of Burgundy; a canoe trip from Paris up the Seine, through the canals and finally down the Loire to Tours, followed by a stroll through the chateau country; a four months' trip through Austria, and so on. Paris accepted such a mood, understood it, as no American city could. I was fortunate to be able to take advantage of such a happy-go-lucky epoch.

My wanderlust becoming less urgent, I married a Philadelphia girl in Paris. Scoop was born. We lived in Paris or in a peasant cottage in the Vallée de Chevreuse, within easy driving distance of my work, and all was pleasant until Hitler's evil star started to rise above the horizon. I was soon convinced that war was inevitable, and in 1937 we packed up and returned to New York. There I joined the staff of the embryonic World's Fair to handle foreign press publicity, then the Office of War Information after Pétain surrendered France to the Nazis. In 1942 I was tapped for a secret mission overseas, and that was just about all I knew about the whole affair until I arrived in Algiers with the invasion, where a Psychological Warfare unit was being established. I engaged in combat radio work, took part in the landings in Sicily and Italy (I stayed in Naples until Rome fell, then moved north to the vicinity of Leghorn) and finally joined the team going into southern France. Once again on French soil, I was strongly tempted to follow the example of some Frenchmen with us who, seeing their native land for the first time in several years, threw themselves flat to kiss the soil. We moved north as the German forces withdrew in chaos, halted in the Vosges region.

In 1918 I had been weeks late for the Armistice celebration in Paris, which must have been one of the great exhibitions of unfettered joy in all history. Even in late December, when I managed to return, there were more than echoes of those glorious days and nights. In 1944, without leave and without leave-taking, I took off with a friend from our camp near Mulhouse, that gray and unbelievably unemotional city, and in a weapons carrier we hastened to Paris, where inhibitions are ever on a lax rein. We were only three days late for the opening festivities but friends, both French and American, were soon located, new friends were made and life was at its highest key.

A couple of mornings later I had an overpowering urge to return to the Chevreuse Valley, to the village of Garnes and the peasant house where Mary and Scoop and I had lived so happily. Off I went in the weapons carrier, over the same road I had driven often when working on newspapers in Paris. I stopped at the *épicerie* in Dampierre, which had delivered groceries to us. M. and Mme. Mestivier were certainly astonished and also delighted when they recognized me in my military garb. They poured a drink. I ordered a round in return. Then I took off, promising to stop on the way back.

Yes, the house was still standing. It was empty now, but it had been taken over by German soldiers for many months during the occupation. The gate to the grounds about the house was reduced to hinges. Weeds and rank grass covered all but a narrow path to the door, beside which still grew the laurel tree from which we had plucked leaves for stews and other dishes. The house was a shambles inside. Dirt, old ration tins, odds and ends littered the floor. In the big fireplace were the partly burned pages of books we had left, books of no great consequence—yet how can one destroy a book, any book whatsoever? Parts of books, bindings ripped off, were scattered over the floor. The bookshelves, which I had installed, were empty. No one, obviously, had thought to return a book to its shelf. The other two rooms were in the same sorry condition, as though only destructive animals had been sheltered there in filth and ignorance.

I was starting out the door, hurrying away, when I recalled a November evening when Mestivier had knocked at the door with his weekly load of supplies. It was November 23, Scoop's fifth birthday. His village pal, Michel, was with us. And Mestivier was transfixed by what he saw, lighted by oil lamps and the fireplace, through the glass panes in the door.

There were Mary and I on our knees on the tile floor, Scoop and Michel likewise, roaring, between shouts of laughter, the old French nursery song of *Savez-vous planter les choux,* or "How to Plant Cabbages." The song can be well-nigh interminable. Cabbages are planted with a finger, the elbow, the shoulder, the lips and on and on. With each chorus the act must be performed on the floor. We were planting with our elbows when Mestivier arrived. Was he shocked, offended by such lack of adult decorum? No Frenchman would be. He deposited his box at the door, walked in, knelt down and away he went.

> *On les plante avec le nez,*
> *On les plante avec le nez,*
> *A la mode de chez nous.*

Planting with our noses placed us in a position of fitting obeisance to neighborliness, friendliness, good cheer.

Surely I had recalled that hilarious incident because of its vivid contrast with the squalid mess before me. And, fortunately, it is still this earlier memory, with so many other equally gay, that remains vivid.

And so back to the Vosges, with the outcome of the war

assured and I with an intense dislike of going into Germany. I applied for leave, obtained it, and flew back to the family in New York for Thanksgiving.

The following spring, when the Psychological Warfare branch was being transformed into the United States Information Service, I was urged to fly to Paris and establish a bureau in Marseilles. Still in the disturbed state that had followed two years spent as a kind of military nomad, wondering what I wanted to do, I accepted, finally persuaded by my fondness for Marseilles. I worked there for a year, then brought Mary and Scoop over. We came to know many people, formed fast friendships with French men and women ranging from artists, writers and journalists to business people and others in the upper social stratum, something almost impossible in Paris but extremely easy in the free and easy atmosphere of Marseilles. All in all, they were two memorable years that ended when Congress voted to curtail the U.S.I.S. budget and the Marseilles bureau had to be closed.

That rather sudden change occurred when the last remnants of my wanderlust were disappearing. I was fifty-three, and the desire to settle down was becoming insistent. I could have stayed on in Europe at a new post but now I wanted to go back home. Mary did too. And Scoop, by this time fluent in French, needed American schooling, especially college. I had played with the idea of farming from time to time, had even inquired into the possibility of making a go of it in France. But it was fairly obvious that American surroundings would be far more favorable to such an undertaking—we packed up, drove to Paris for a brief farewell and sailed for New York.

While Mary stayed with her sister on Long Island, Scoop and I took the old Ford, a 1939 sedan which I still drive, and set forth on the great quest. After numerous disappointments, looking at rundown or abandoned farms that were depressing at first glance, we came to the present High Meadows and promptly fell in love with it. And here we are, still on the same hilltop, after nearly fourteen years.

Appraising such a career with an impartial eye, I cannot imagine one more removed from agricultural pursuits, one offering less promise of even a modest success. Yet the records are public. And in an upset world they reveal that anything can happen. Success has not been overwhelming. That, however, I never did expect. Enough that the big jump from concrete sidewalks to yielding earth can be made without starving. In fact, one can put on a little unwanted weight.

I have come to debating with myself whether my farm ever would have been sold to a real farmer, one who had labored with the earth and could absorb in one sweeping glance the favorable and unfavorable aspects of a farm. Such a man sees the land as a strictly practical entity, a constant challenge to muscle and mind, with no place for esthetic values—the lure of lovely rolling hills, say, surrounding woods of varicolored pattern provided haphazardly by different kinds of trees from the rich green of hemlock and pine to the dusty green of black locust. No, woods are regarded with a calculating eye as a source of salable timber or logs that can be transported to a nearby sawmill and reduced to boards and joists for which there is an endless need around the barn and shed. And sloping fields once were manageable with the slow labor of horses, but today the faster-moving tractor with the various heavy machinery it takes in tow is much more efficient on level ground.

Contrariwise, a view, a wide vista, was an essential requirement for *our* country home, one freeing us as much as possible

19

from the monotony of nearby walls and windows, even the restricted outlook of suburbia. Yet the man who knows about land notes immediately that a view of several miles means a hilltop, that magnificent sunsets are had only when the entire western sector of the compass is without shelter or windbreak. The same for sunrises in the east. Such exposure means strong winds in summer which hamper, even halt, haying or other harvesting. And in winter the west and northwest winds bring bitter cold, snow heaped about barn doors, chilly barns where the livestock is quartered, frozen water pipes.

The hilltop establishment also meets the unyielding opposition of the professional farmer's wife, for the above reasons and an additional one, to her just as important as the others. She wants, she demands in no moot terms, a road that is kept open in all but the worst winter weather. She insists on her right to take the car out when she so desires, whether for visiting friends or for collecting provender, and also the truck, which she handles just as efficiently as her husband, when she is called upon to fetch a load of feed or fertilizer. Moreover, she plays a game that fascinates me. She knows every locally owned vehicle, car, truck or tractor, distinguishes at a glance, beyond my understanding, between two cars of the same make, model, paint job, everything except the license plate. She can be busy about the kitchen or apparently any other room in the house, yet never miss the identity of some kind of locomotion that whisks by at thirty to forty miles an hour. It is a game, a challenge to her, and she refuses to be denied it. Also, it adds a bit of chatter the next time she calls a friend on the party line.

She, I am sure, would never agree to the seclusion of my hilltop. Her farmer husband would quickly have diagnosed the problems inherent in my pleasantly sloping fields, my hill road that would surely be blocked by snow in winter. What I counted as blessings they would have unanimously voted as drawbacks they would prefer to do without. I strongly suspect that High Meadows was bound to remain on the "For Sale" list until a city feller like me stumbled on it.

And yet, after three weeks of looking at farms for sale, Scoop and I were elated when we drove up the hill and into the lane. The house possessed little charm—it was just another two-story frame building with white paint flaking off here and there—yet it offered a roomy porch, a big kitchen with a coal and wood range, a dining room, a living room and a side room, with four bedrooms upstairs and a bathroom, hot and cold running water, a large cellar and a hot-air furnace. All quite acceptable. Immediately we envisioned improvements that would provide a more pleasing effect.

But it was outdoors that our enthusiasm began to soar. The big imposing barn impressed us at once as being in good condition and ready for business; likewise, several sheds and poultry houses. And on the east a large field, part of the farm, drew a level line for the horizon, while to the west, beyond the adjoining valley, wooded hills and ridges were visible in close array for at least ten miles—an incomparable arrangement for sunsets. Finally, it was a going farm, operated by the nephew of the owner, who had died. The field to the east was lush with clover, the other fields were well kept. The farm was bounded east, south and north by its own fields and woods, and there was that wonderful panorama to the west. It seemed to be made for us. We bought it.

Thus we acquired all the essentials we had listed: a spring which we were assured had never run dry and which was piped to the house; our own land on three sides to guarantee privacy and on the other the wide and splendid opening to the west, where the only visible farm was a mile distant; an adequate house, with bath and toilet, not always present in old farm houses where the privy is still common, and a furnace. Ah, what the eye can quickly add to give glamor to plainness; what the imagination, taking off in full flight from very slender incentive, can achieve in transforming mediocrity into resplendence! Merlin's wand can't compete with vision turned visionary, altering in less than the trice it took Merlin to spin and vanish, walls, floors, paint, every dull, depressing aspect of a place, imbuing it with the magic of the future so that all glows with charm and allure, a shelter without rival, a foyer of good cheer, hospitality and repose.

Scoop returned to New York for school and though it took two weeks for the final papers to be certified, I was allowed the freedom of the place. They were lovely October days, the afternoon sun still warm, the autumnal haze draping the woods while leaves fell, branches returned to somnolent bareness, fields lost their green. Day after day, I sat on the porch, dreamy in the warmth, noting what should be done here, what might be done there, and there and there. The porch could be mended, even enlarged; fresh white paint brightened with yellow trim would make the house far more attractive; that spacious kitchen would match nobly my desire for simplicity and rustic cheer. Stale clichés suddenly had a fresh appeal: murmur of coals burning in the big iron range, exuding a friendly glow and warmth, ashes sifting softly from the firebox, a pot bubbling happily on the back of the stove. All this became reality whenever I gazed about the otherwise empty, damp and musty room. Breakfast before the sunny east window would be an auspicious start for any day, and what could be more enticing than that warm and odorous kitchen on a frosty, snowy night after the day's work was done? I hadn't figured just what that work would be on a frosty, snowy day, but never mind. It would have been done.

Who, eager to exchange noisy, crowded city life for the serenity and independence of a farm, has not been equally guilty of such fantasy and romancing, with little if any appreciation of the flimsy foundation on which they are to be realized? Given the eagerness, the dreams are inevitable.

As I say, we got precisely the farm we had in mind. Moreover, many of the dreams have come true. Nearly fourteen full years of dairying on my hilltop have been vastly rewarding in innumerable ways. But at what a cost in woes, setbacks, brief as well as enduring disasters, and frequently the ultimate depths of despair! Every farmer, even the best, experiences disappointments and heartbreaks. But I differ from him in one particular. He possesses a mentality which has long since accepted the bad with the good as an inescapable part of farming, a kind of forfeit that must be paid to obtain the good. And even when the balance is against him, when the forfeit becomes a harsh, inexorable penalty, he may groan loudly, complain bitterly, but he fights on, certain that somehow the balance will be restored. That frame of mind I have not been able to achieve, though fourteen years represent a long training period. In recent years, especially, I tend to scan with prejudiced eye the debit column and decide that, year in and year out, it runs longer and redder than the blackish gray of the credit column. Perhaps my sixty-seven years are apt to exaggerate in totting up the total in red, though physically I am thoroughly fit. Perhaps it is just my temperament asserting itself now that all the initial challenges have been met and overcome. Perhaps I have gained my share of rewards and incline to regard them as my due with a minimum of effort, an unforgivable form of smugness. I haven't yet decided. Maybe I will be a little clearer when I finish composing this rural requiem for twelve cows.

2.

THE PRICE OF INNOCENCE, or ignorance, is high. For several years I paid that price, with usurious interest. And it was the cows that sustained me when trials and disappointments seemed without end. Through every crisis, every new and unforeseen catastrophe, I could look at them and take heart, slowly rise again in morale to meet the next test of my endurance. In the barn or on pasture they exuded patience, unconcern, an imperturbability that could not help registering on my overwrought nerves and reducing tension until a calm approximating theirs was restored to me. In my book they are the noblest of all domestic animals. I like horses, dogs, cats; I find young pigs extravagantly comic, young goats likewise; I am indifferent to sheep and chickens. True, one can make a living with any of these domestic specimens along with whatever affection they inspire. But I find they cannot compare with the good cow, raised from birth with understanding and gentleness, that comes into her productive prime at about five years and for at least another five years will give generously of that rich milk which can amount to a net profit of $250 per cow per year.

Cows, obviously, should be comfortably quartered and not only adequately but intelligently fed. Yet comfort is not always assured despite precautions. A window light may loosen and fall out as the wind shoves and sucks at it. A steady blast of cold air then blows directly into the faces of the nearby cows. Do they mind? Just as serenely as ever they chew their cuds, poke their long curling tongues into one nostril, then the other, and gaze tranquilly into some bovine world, of which I know nothing though it apparently is pleasant.

At one time the barn had a makeshift lean-to shed along the west wall, intended for calves, which helped to support a kind of balcony that added extra headroom for the horses when they hauled a load of hay onto the ramp between the mows. A gusty March wind, aided by deep snow on the shed roof, caused it all to collapse. This left a large opening at the end of the ramp where snow accumulated and melted when the afternoon sun reached it. This dripped directly down and onto the heads of the four cows stanchioned beneath—a steady, chilly splashing, in greater volume when March rain replaced the snow. The cows blinked, shook their heads occasionally, otherwise were much more interested in their hay. And there was no ill effect on their milk. There have been times also when the barn was so cold that water froze in the drinking cups, necessitating my going round with a pail of boiling water and thawing them out; once the water pipes in the barn froze it was so cold.

Barn doors, the kind suspended from rollers on a steel trolley, can be very tricky. In severe weather I am in a hurry to get doors open and closed; and if snow is deep along the barn wall I am inclined to take a chance that the door, with a quick heave, will plow through the snow. But, as in all gambles, it doesn't always do so. Instead, one end rides up on the snow, the roller is forced off the rail—and there the door is, half-open, one end sagging with nothing to hold it, while the bitter wind streams into the barn with an avenging moan. Then the packed snow must be cleared away and the door hauled along until the freed roller has been brought to the end of the rail and slipped back onto the track—not as easy as it sounds, especially in the dark. Meanwhile, the temperature, where the cows are quartered, has dropped five, maybe ten degrees. The obvious lesson is: Don't take such chances. But temptation is strong when fingers are already numb and hunger, whetted by icy blasts, is keen for hot food. And always the cows accepted such unpleasant experiences without complaint.

However, let's leave the cows for the moment and examine more closely this, in our ecstatic opinion, very nearly ideal farm, and what was revealed in proving the pudding. Start with the house. Since it had sheltered three or more generations of the same family, the assumption would be warranted that it was reasonably snug and livable for hardy farming people; and, indeed, on those warm October days when I wandered from room to room planning alterations, it was. The somewhat dim interior, with an occasional fly buzzing and a wasp banging its silly head against a window, was inviting, perhaps the more so because, empty as it was, I found it easy to visualize our own furniture enhancing the rooms. But how to realize that the papered walls were of rough planks with cracks between and that the outer siding was old and warped, leaving innumerable interstices for cold wind to filter through? How to know that the old-fashioned windows, with stops in the sides that slipped into holes in the frames, were loose enough to rattle in a strong breeze so that to stand next to one on a cold day was just one brief remove from going outdoors?

The hot-air furnace boasted just one register, a big one nearly a yard square, from which one could easily imagine a huge column of heat rising with such force that it would fill every room with greenhouse temperature. True, there was a single small opening in the ceiling, just above it, to provide heat for all the upstairs, but the open stairway itself, surely, would be a broad channel up which a river of heat would flow, following that elementary thermal law that hot air must rise. I don't question the veracity of that law but I have learned that a vast quantity of heat, approximating what a blast furnace would provide, is needed to drive that hot air upstairs. I have stood over that big register, shirttail out to trap heat along my back, until I was pleasantly warm, only to be chilled at the end of the five steps between register and bed. For I was alone that first winter, which was one of the bitterest on record, and was not long in deciding to put a bed in the room off the living room. Moreover, don't think I shed that shirt during that brief trip. On the coldest nights I didn't even remove my dungarees, only my shoes.

Down cellar, along with the furnace, was a kind of water heater new to me, known as a "bucket a day." What it was was a small, pot-bellied stove that heated water in a connected iron tank. What's more, it actually did, provided it was kept up to proper peak. But it was an erratic unit, given to moods, sometimes sensitive to drafts, sometimes quite oblivious of them. Unpredictably, it was always either too hot or too cool. Frequently, having religiously fed it the prescribed bucket in the morning I would find it burned out by afternoon. Or it would still be stoked high and barely simmering, the water hardly tepid. Hence, drawing a really hot bath in the chilly bathroom, vaguely warmed by one of those smelly, smoky, portable kerosene stoves, was a genuine achievement requiring precise adjustment of the draft on the "bucket a day" heater so that it burned fast but not too fast, feeling the tank to make sure of the temperature and the quantity of hot water, and finally, at the all-important moment, tossing a little extra coal into the stove. Then upstairs I would bolt, undressing while steamy water flowed all too slowly into the tub. It had to be steaming because the iron tub was so cold that the first few gallons of water were chilled on contact. Oh well, I didn't take many baths that winter, anyway.

In the spring, when the cows were out on pasture, I got involved in one improvement that can best be likened to bailing out a boat with a sieve. The living room floor was almost completely covered with worn, cracked linoleum of an ugly brown color. So, in my spare time, I ripped it up, dug out endless tacks and laid bare a plank floor, the planks varying in width from a foot to nearly two feet. Could be quite handsome, quoth I, if properly finished. Thereupon I rented a sanding machine to put a smooth surface on the planks. That, however, was not eminently satisfactory for the planks were of hemlock and in many spots where the grain was just right— or all wrong in my opinion—the surface would shred, becoming rougher than ever instead of acquiring that satin-smooth gloss I was questing for. Nevertheless, a very general improvement was noticeable and I felt reasonably rewarded for my labor until I noticed that the dust and the shreds were stirring here and there, even puffing up in tiny clouds. Puzzled, I glanced around to see if doors or windows were open. They were not, and I knelt down for closer inspection—only to discover cracks between the planks, running their entire length and as much as a quarter-inch in width! I peered through the widest and . . . saw the cellar floor! One more source of cold air in winter, partly stoppered by dirt and that old linoleum, now laid bare, wide and handsome, by my toil.

The only remedy that seemed equal to the problem was to caulk the cracks, as on a boat deck or hull. I sent off a hurried letter to the painter Waldo Peirce, a long-time friend and a native of Maine, where, after all, boats are almost as essential as automobiles. I explained my predicament and my possible solution and requested a large supply of tow and pitch. Waldo responded with alacrity and again I set to work. Despite the greatest care, however, when I poked tow into the wider cracks and attempted to install it firmly enough to hold pitch, it would often get pushed too far, even beyond retrieving, so that when I examined the result from the viewpoint of the cellar my only impression was that somehow pale yellow Spanish moss had started to grow and was draping itself above me in curls, festoons, serpentines and arabesques.

Eventually, however, I reached the stage for pouring pitch. This I heated on the kitchen range, poured it into a can the rim of which I had bent with pliers to form a very narrow pouring lip and decided all was ready. But, the can being too hot to pick up with my bare hands, I donned heavy work gloves. Then I knelt down before the widest crack, neatly stuffed with tow . . . I will never undertake that job again, unless I devise or discover a better system. The pitch wouldn't flow evenly, and as my hands got hotter I found it impossible to keep the pitch flowing and at the same time follow the all-too-straight line between the planks. Blobs appeared here and there; the stream of pitch would waver to form lean black snakes that persistently crossed and recrossed the crack. Frequently it was too heavy for the tow and ran straight through to the cellar. And, after setting down the can of pitch to cool my fingers, I was rarely able to start again with a flow of pitch that matched the width where I had left off. All in all, rather messy. So I compromised, did my best around the perimeter of the room and voted to cover the rest with rugs as adequately as possible.

Mary and Scoop came out for that first Christmas, hardly recognizing me at the station because of the pounds I had moulted in a couple of months, and we had a rousing holiday, not diminished a whit by cold bedrooms, possibly even enhanced by celebrating almost entirely in the big, warm kitchen.

It would be mostly repetitious to describe more intimate acquaintance with the barn. It was old, and innumerable holes, cracks and apertures permitted the almost constant arctic northwest wind to finger its way in and keep down temperatures. For the moment that drawback, serious as it was, had to be lived with, which the cows and I did, precarious as it became on numerous occasions before spring.

And then there was the lie of the land—the wooded ridge to the south, the higher elevation of East Meadow, its adjoining pasture. It was all so pleasing to behold that first fall, the sun seeming to leap direct from the soil, the tall trees hospitably beckoning, beneath which long-fallen leaves, richly hued mosses, outcroppings of lichen-blanketed rocks, the scattering of wild flowers, made walking alluring. *Entrancing* could be a suitable adjective for it. In my less benign moments, *diabolic* is more appropriate.

Here is the geological pattern. The barn extends directly north and south, the big back door to the south and, in front of it, a narrow level strip for turning vehicles around. Beyond that a three-acre field rises, occasionally at a pitch of twenty-five degrees. At its southern rim lies an intervening patch, mostly brambles, too difficult to cultivate. Then another three-acre field continues the upward slope though less abruptly. Once up there one has a splendid view of a broad sweep of country, farmhouses, fields and woods. Now back to the barn. To the east runs a stone-walled lane which turns sharply right, or south, to follow the walled edge of the first field, then again sharp right just within the woods to make a steep climb to the second field and also, farther up, to a fine growth of sugar maples. (The second field was soon dubbed "Hell's Acres" because it was hard to work and bringing a load of hay down from it along the fast-sloping trail was definitely perilous to a novice with a team of horses that could not be held back when the load of hay started to urge them on. Frequently they broke into a full gallop around the turns and eventually up the ramp between the hay mows.) The whole ridge to the south extends all the way to the boundary line at the far side of East Meadow. Thus, all land south and east of the barn stands above it and slopes toward it, the walled lane forming a perfect, man-made channel to guide rain and melting snow directly to both ends of the barn—though not against the long east wall, formed by a bank of stone and earth, which splits the water into two currents. It would have taken an engineer's trained eye to grasp the potential of that layout. I am not an engineer and had to learn the hard way—that that section of my lovely landscape was a natural funnel with the barn at the not-so-narrow end.

The "never-failing" spring also deserves some attention. In the strictly literal sense its reputation is unmarred. It never has gone dry despite a number of prolonged arid spells that transformed earth into a simulacrum of concrete, turned green fields into dun wastes. Always there was a perceptible trickle that flowed from some subterranean reservoir in the southern ridge and into the springhouse vat, whence it was pumped into a pressure tank in the house cellar and on to the barn as needed. But cows quite understandably are thirsty beasts. When they are producing seven to eight gallons of milk daily they need more than twice that amount of water, both for milk and for bodily requirements. By evening of a hot day, when they come from waterless pasture to the barn to be milked (I possess only one pasture with a brook) they battle greedily for the drinking bowls, one for every two cows. One will get her big muzzle in a bowl and suck noisily and most tantalizingly despite the frantic efforts of her neighbor, using horns and powerful shoves, to oust her. A few knowing ones, especially at the end of the line where there is little if any water until those farther up have had their fill, stoically bide their time until water again flows freely, then blissfully bury their noses in the bowls, swallowing great gulps without letup for minutes on end.

Very evidently, a thin stream of supply cannot keep up with such insatiable demand. There were a few occasions, then, when I was obliged to haul water in milk cans and have them ready at the springhouse. After an interval of thirst-quenching, the length of which I came to judge with fair accuracy, I would rush to the springhouse, find the vat nearly empty and dump water into it. A milk can holds ten gallons, so that five or six cans generally sufficed, provided the tank was full when the cows came to the barn. During the worst dry periods as much as three hours might be required to fill it, and woe to the thoughtless person who turned on water at the house during that period. (I should add that there is an old well, more than thirty feet deep, beside the house which once boasted a pump and supplied water for the household in old days. I have had this hooked up with the pump and pressure tank for emergency use. It has been a boon on frequent occasions, but since it does not replenish itself in a bad drought, it goes dry after a few days of repeated use.)

Yes, High Meadows has its full share of drawbacks, and I have come to confess as much when hard-pressed to do so, though I still resent with a show of temper such deprecation coming from someone else. Yet other hilltop farms have comparable faults and disadvantages, and those valley freeholds that are spared such deficiencies as mine are damned with others, if only such a top-bracket one, to me, as three hours' less sunlight per day than I enjoy. Moreover, only once or twice a springtime does my lane rival a full-blown torrent; the northwest wind does not blow perpetually; snowdrifts are inevitably doomed to disappear; and droughts come to an end with blessed rain. Hurricanes have wreaked their damage, nature at one time or another has played what must be every trick in her capacious bag, yet luck is good as well as bad, and High Meadows is still with me and I am still with it, more emphatically than ever.

Mentioning luck leads me to interpolate a few remarks, before getting on with this pastoral saga, about a sample of bad luck that turned into amazing good.

During the war and until I returned from overseas in 1947, I did not pay income taxes because of a special wartime ruling. A volunteer in psychological warfare, I worked with the U.S. Army but as a civilian with what was known as "assimilated" rank, meaning that with my eventual rank of lieutenant colonel I enjoyed most of the official privileges of the actual army officer even though I wore no insignia. I could wear a uniform or civilian clothes, depending mainly on where I happened to be stationed. At the front with a combat radio unit, a uniform was more practical. But I remained in Algiers, Tunis, Palermo or Naples for as much as six months at a stretch, helping to establish radio programs for the local public, censoring newspapers with subversive inclinations, and preparing and dispensing news itself as communication facilities were disrupted or became nonexistent after each campaign ended. In other words, when at or close to the front, I lived the same rough life as army people, while in the cities I and everyone else in the occupying forces managed to enjoy somewhat greater comfort though we were nevertheless under military control.

Memories are still fresh of that ever-changing epoch: working with staunchly democratic French residents of Algiers in opposition to the strong fascist and pro-Pétain groups; getting a wonderful old Sicilian in Tunis to read his earthy peasant poetry which we beamed to Sicily before the invasion; in Naples, putting on the air San Carlo opera productions which doubtless lacked top singing talent but which delighted the Neapolitans, even, I am sure, lifted their morale.

This, however, is beside the point I must come to.

When I got back to the United States and to High Meadows I complied with the law and submitted details of my situation to the Revenue Bureau, having been informed that war service overseas such as mine was exempt from income tax with certain reservations. Some time later a revenue field man came to the house with the papers I had filed, discussed them all with me and agreed that he saw no reason for payment of income tax for the years in question. I was glad to have such assurance, naturally, then forgot the matter. After a month or so another "revenooer" appeared and, with an attitude of finally having caught up with a criminal, told me I owed the government approximately $2,500. I was so utterly astounded that all I could think—and keep muttering—was that I would have to give up the farm, that I had no such sum of money as $2,500 and knew of no way to obtain it. I was not exaggerating, but it made no impression on my visitor. He told me that a schedule of monthly payments would be worked out with another field man whom I was to see without delay at the county seat. And he departed.

I was truly in despair. Income from the cows was barely enough to pay my bills; my bank account had been greatly depleted by unavoidable expenditures. However, when I calmed down and sized up all aspects of the crisis, I discovered a thin ray of hope. If I could keep payments to a minimum for the next year, my financial situation should improve. At the very worst I could sell one cow and keep hanging on. I swore I would not give up the farm itself.

The going was tough for several months, always with the sense that I was being hounded. I was even told from time to time that I wasn't cooperative, that the tax bureau was being very lenient. When I got furious and told the agent what I thought of such blood-sucking methods, I only met with the intimation that my payments could be increased. He even told me during one scene that he suspected strongly that I had money stashed away somewhere and could easily pay more. "When you find it let me know, I sure can use it," I replied. I pondered that near-accusation that I was lying for several days and came up with what I am certain was the reasoning behind his statement. I don't look like a farmer and I never will. I don't act or speak like a farmer. It is an aura no city-bred person can acquire in a lifetime. I wore dungarees, work shoes, old clothes; nevertheless, in no way did I possess the air of a penurious country man. In the agent's opinion, accordingly, my story did not jibe in any way with the impression I gave him.

Constantly casting about for some scheme to make a little extra money, I recalled that when I bought the farm the general description of it included an abandoned quarry for flagstone. I had inspected it occasionally on my rambles around my estate, but it seemed nothing more than a bramble-filled hole in the ground that promised precisely nothing. I had learned, of course, that flagstone quarries were frequently found in the region and that they were worked by the owner or leased, with a royalty to the owner. Now inquiring further, I gathered information about several quarry men, including one named Lee A. Wilbur, who everyone said was honest. The initials L. A. W. seemed a good omen and I asked him for an opinion. He doubted the possibility of finding marketable stone but agreed to look over the spot. He pecked away in the old hole with hammer and pinch-bar; then, just for good measure, knocked dirt loose in another direction and came upon a face of stone. A little more work and enough stone was bared—layer upon layer of what he was sure was flagstone, the seams, or reaves in quarry parlance, running straight and even all the way across. Satisfied with what he saw he promised to return the next day with more tools.

The end of the story smacks of a Ripley "Believe It or Not" yarn. That quarry turned into one of the best in the county— beautiful blue flagstone, regular in thickness, almost billiard-table smooth on one side, all coming up with little effort in big sheets easily cut to suitable size. After the first year with only a few men, it expanded till as many as thirty men were at work. I was stupid not to realize that a crew of such size could not be supervised properly, and there was a considerable loss of salable stone simply because the men did not take sufficient care in freeing and cutting it. Hence, it ran out in less than three years, leaving a huge pile of broken stone which neighbors and I still go to for rejected irregular pieces that can be cut and used for terraces, steps, outdoor fireplaces, etc. But before it was exhausted it not only paid that damnable back income tax but obliged me to pay more income tax on the royalties it brought in.

Even that is not the end of my flagstone story. Two years ago a young stone worker whom I had known slightly when he worked in my quarry, said that his brother had once been a hired man for the deceased owner of my farm and had told him that, when plowing in the upper corner of Hell's Acres, he frequently turned up large pieces of flagstone. And he asked my permission to look about for signs of more stone, which, of course, I granted. Such a spot, like the old quarry, would be remote from the house, hidden by trees, and could not be a nuisance in any way. That same day I met neighbor Richard and asked his opinion of the prospect since he had grown up on the farm and undoubtedly had plowed the same field many times. He admitted there might be a possibility of more flagstone, for his father had used flagstone from up there for the present flooring in the cellar. The upshot was the opening of a small quarry on the ridge, now operated by one man who sets a slow, steady pace that is to my liking. I doubt that it will ever be important, for it appears to be a narrow strip of flagstone that runs along the ridge. Nevertheless, it brings me a few dollars every year which are pleasant to turn to when repairs are necessary or some unforeseen expenditure arises.

I still wonder at times whether I would have been able to remain at High Meadows without that veritable gold mine that opened for me at such a critical moment. Certainly I would have faced a long and highly irritating struggle to pay off those taxes, the kind I would have resented deeply day after day and which so easily weakens the will to fight. On the whole I am pretty well convinced that I would have made it. The dairy business was improving year by year, I was more capable as a dairy farmer. Yet who can say with finality "Yes" or "No"?

3.

THREE IMPORTANT CHANGES were made later at High Meadows and they contributed notably to better living. The first, chronologically, came early in March, 1950, when the house burned down. Mary had not yet arrived to greet the spring and I recall writing to her. "Here is bad news. The house burned down, completely." What else could I say? There is no way to soften the jolt of such dreadful news. An ugly fact might just as well be announced with ugly bluntness.

I was in the house when it started, going over some papers in the bedroom-study. Suddenly I was aware of a strange crackling from the kitchen, got up to investigate and found one kitchen wall in flames that were moving hungrily toward the ceiling. Paralyzed momentarily, I finally leaped out the kitchen door, yelling "Fire! Fire!" at the top of my voice, but realizing the utter impossibility of making it carry all the distance—of which we had frequently boasted—that isolated us from neighbors. I grabbed an empty pail and rushed back into the kitchen to fill it at the sink—another near-futile gesture because of the time it took to get a pailful. The flames were now in the ceiling—dry, flimsy wood that seemed to ignite even before the fire reached it. I dashed upstairs, thinking it would help to fill the washbowl to overflowing so that water would seep through the floor. But up there the water pressure was still weaker. The smoke by now was so thick that I had to get out. Again I ran outdoors to call for help. I recall how angry I got at Susquie, the dog, who ran back and forth with me, barking, leaping about, elated that I was playing a new game. The kitchen, obviously, was beyond saving. When I threw the pail of water, that had filled meanwhile, it merely vanished in steam.

Then help began to arrive. Neighbors, attracted by the smoke and flame, appeared and we started to haul out furniture, indeed everything movable. The siren of the local volunteer fire engine wailed slowly up the hill, where snow and a few cars hampered movement. A hose was swiftly in operation, using water from the engine's emergency tank. The only other source of water was the springhouse, but that was completely inadequate for the big hose in use. Amid all the excitement, the hurrying about, I remembered the old well beside the house, capped with concrete for many years. Undismayed, a lusty volunteer picked up a sledge and in a few moments had banged a hole through the concrete. The well was full of water and for a brief interval it did its best, but this was still far short of what was needed. All too plainly, the house was beyond saving. So, cherishing the remaining water, we turned the hose on the barn wall facing the house. Fortunately, there was no wind—the prevailing northwesterly would have carried sparks and embers toward the barn. As it was, the heat was already so great that the whole wall of the barn steamed furiously when the water hit. But it survived.

The house was now going through its final convulsions. The roof began to fall in; one wall, then another, collapsed—all very neatly into the cellar within the foundation walls. Thus, an entire eight-room dwelling was reduced to some twisted metal and two pick-up truckloads of ashes.

Almost everything downstairs was saved, but some furniture, lots of clothing, and several valued paintings were in those ashes—and, for the moment, a big, ever-expanding dream.

The crowd soon dispersed, the fire engine pulled out, one neighbor took me aside and ordered me to take a huge drink from a flask of whisky. I did, but it had little effect. Another, with remarkable forethought, had called the electric light company, and before dark a lineman arrived and installed a direct wire from the power pole to the barn so that there was electricity there for milking. I tried to stay to milk the cows but was ordered away by friends who took over that chore while another drove me to a doctor who treated some big blisters on my forehead and hands but could do nothing for a lot of hair that had been singed off. And my neighbors and by now close friends, Richard and Bea, insisted on taking me in for the night and as long as I cared to stay.

Fire in the country is a hellish affair, so hellish that it immediately becomes a communal concern. Even people I scarcely recognized proved more than willing to pitch in and help in any manner required, for every farmer recognizes it as a threat that hangs over him as well as all others. The day might come when he would need such help himself. The final gesture for me was for a squad of farmers to bring up a couple of trucks and in one day shovel all the debris from the

42

cellar and haul it away—except for the coal bin, where a couple of tons of coal burned merrily for more than a week.

The evening of the fire, after dinner with Richard and Bea, I cooled off sufficiently to consider the situation and discuss it with them. Old electrical wiring appeared to be the most probable cause, which was of little importance to me. That was in the past. What about the future? The house was insured for $4,000. How much would a new house cost? How long for the building? Should I count such a setback as final warning that the fates did not intend me to be a farmer? Thoughts, possibilities, probabilities churned around in my head, mostly of a very somber hue. Would it be months before I would again have a home? Could I manage the farm properly in such circumstances? Maybe there was a hex on the place. Would it be wiser to take the insurance money, sell the cows and the farm (not worth much without a house) and try again elsewhere? What would Mary wish to do, she who was little more than lukewarm about living in the country in any case. What to do? What to do?

Some progress toward a decision was made that first evening. I phoned the best of the local carpenters and asked if he would come around the following morning and discuss the matter. He agreed and the conference was held at Bea's immaculate kitchen table. On a piece of wrapping paper I drew the foundation walls, still solid, of course, with their approximate measurements, a very thick L-shape. We took turns sketching in rooms, arranging them and rearranging them. We debated an upstairs for bedrooms. Don—the carpenter—offered valuable suggestions about materials, and when we had agreed on a rough provisional plan, he started figuring costs, down to every essential detail. When he had totted it up and checked it over with great care, he announced, almost apologetically for the size of the sum, that he and his helper could do the job for some $4,500, adding that with reasonably good weather, the house would be finished in about six weeks. Wiring, plumbing, furnace were not included, and they would bring the total to some $5,500.

This was not nearly such bad news as Don had apparently feared it would be to me. I was sure I could borrow $1,000 from the bank. The remaining $500 could be managed somehow. Without any hesitation I called it a deal. And the insurance money was paid in full, five days after the fire.

That was an astonishing piece of building, a shining example of what a good artisan, taking great pride in his work, willing to maintain a fast yet skilful pace, can accomplish in a comparatively short time. Snow on the ground, cold March winds, the occasional snowfall—conditions that so many workmen would balk at—were taken in smooth stride by Don and his capable helper, Kenny. I served as liaison man between Don and the building supply outfit some eight miles distant. My job was to make certain that materials were delivered in proper quantity precisely as needed so that lumber and other necessities were not exposed to wet weather for too long a period. Cooperation was excellent and everything progressed most satisfactorily.

I still find it hard to believe, but on March 21 the future kitchen was sufficiently covered to permit installation of a bottled-gas stove (which we still use) on which I could cook a hot lunch. Blankets were hung to bar drafts along the passage to the front of the house, which at this time was so open that Don had several choices when it came to moving in material. I can still hear Don yelling, when the odor of frying onions for a spaghetti sauce or a skillet of chili con carne reached him, "Hey, George! When the hell do we eat?" And evenings when they knocked off work and I was preparing to go to the barn for milking, we would sit on nail kegs in the kitchen and talk over a glass or two of bourbon, taken straight and in very sizable portions. So I lived while the house grew around and above me.

Parts of the house, particularly the upstairs, were finally planned as the work progressed. For days we argued over the most convenient place for the cellar stairs and the stairway to the second floor. Even Richard became interested and made several sketches to support his theories. Eventually we combined the two, and for the life of me I cannot imagine why we wasted so much time bickering over a solution that now appears to be the only simple and possible one. But we did. The second floor also went through numerous phases of planning. I had to keep close tab on expenses and paid for material almost on delivery so that I knew my financial standing as work advanced. A full-height second floor with some kind of attic was the most logical structure, but I discovered that it would add markedly to expenses. But outer walls only half the height would keep costs within the budget. I therefore suggested dormer windows, recalling small rooms I had occupied many times in France and in which I found dormers added considerable charm. Don mulled over the idea as he sipped his whiskey and found no objection. The result is three fine bedrooms with ample headroom for a considerable space in the middle of each but with the ceiling sloping down the sides, in which the dormers are set. The bathroom posed another problem. Not only was it difficult to fit in upstairs, but also that required a lot of extra plumbing. Well, why not have a small kitchen with a small bathroom off it? Calipers were almost required to measure every fraction of an inch into which the stove, a good-sized sink, a wall and a full built-in bathtub could be fitted, but Don achieved the miracle. Not exactly customary, I suppose, but very convenient and I have never heard guests object.

Before April reached the halfway mark I moved a single bed, the one I had used prior to the fire, into the bedroom over the kitchen, the smallest of three but sufficient for my needs. It was cold, but I made out with plenty of blankets. Also, though I could never be grateful enough for the shelter provided by Richard and Bea for more than a month, I was now close to my work, I could eat whenever spare time permitted, and I was back home, in my own house.

There was no lack of jobs. As siding went up I followed with paint pot and brush, applying a primer coat before dampness could enter the new wood. And within that siding, I was happy to know, were three additional shields of insulation, thick composition board, ship-lapped, thick bats of rock wool, and the sheet-rock panels that comprised the inner walls. The latter is not to my mind a completely satisfactory substitute for plaster, which possesses a texture, a feeling all its own from being applied by human hands—just as rugs I had found in North Africa showed occasional faults in pattern when some bemused weaver skipped a piece of design and thereby gave much greater appeal than an unerring machine-made product —but a skilled plasterer was not to be found in the region and sheet rock was much less expensive and quickly nailed up. Windows were installed downstairs, including two big aluminum frames on the west wall of the living room. Later, Scoop and a college pal of his used the horses to haul stone with a stone-boat for the big fireplace in the living room, replete with raised hearth of what was truly our native flagstone. The electrician-plumber arrived, wandered about asking where to install outlets, which required considerable thought on my part as I tried to visualize the disposition of furniture, the need for many lamps when the three of us decided to read at the same time. Then on with the plumbing—sink, tub with shower, so greatly missed in the old house, toilet, wash basin, finally the new pump and pressure tank—and water flowed in kitchen and bathroom and barn, the old water pipes from spring to house and house to barn having been untouched by the fire. With the new furnace set up and a far better heating arrangement worked out, the hired work came to an end. I was left to take over all the painting, inside and out, to sand floors and varnish them, and to build bookcases which continue to expand year by year. And the day came when furniture was moved in, pictures were hung, books put in place, rugs laid down.

What profound pleasure filled me as I walked from room to room! A solid house, as weatherproof as a house could be, an attractive house, unpretentious but inviting, a house I would be quite content to end my days in. The old saying goes that to have a full life a man must have a child, build a house and write a book. I didn't actually build the house but I had been so intimately involved in every phase of its building, had even driven nails on occasion, that I felt I could gloss over the purely literal meaning and claim that I had fulfilled all three goals.

In addition to the $4,000 of insurance money the house cost $1,500. That much money invested in improving the old place, or twice, even three times, that sum, would not have produced a thoroughly satisfactory, livable abode. The old plank shell simply was not sufficiently stable to hold up under all the construction that would have been necessary. Moreover, as Don remarked several times, it was a good thing the old place burned completely; for if half of it had been saved, any attempt to rebuild on it would have been costly and still not worth the expense. So, horrible as those first few hours of fire were, I claim I wound up with a remarkable bargain. None of the endless problems encountered by Mr. Blanding; honest, skilled work performed according to estimate and right on schedule; an eminently pleasing place to live in—all for an outlay of $1,500. I fail to see how one could do better.

Such is the tale of the first great change to take place at High Meadows, forced upon me but now so welcome. The second was my decision to dispose of the horses and replace them with a jeep. I had used jeeps frequently during the war and held them in high esteem for wading through deep sand, or mud, climbing out of steep ravines, keeping mobile in just about any terrain and on any road or trail made almost unrecognizable by war. My esteem has never wavered since.

After a few years with the horses I could not help regretting their shortcomings. Molly was a fine, willing mare despite her age of some eighteen years. But the big, gawky gelding I had bought to work with her was far from her equal. He made me laugh repeatedly over some of his silly actions, and there was something free and uninhibited about him when he ripped around a pasture at top speed out of sheer equine joy, head high, mane and tail straight out. However, a load of hay was a different matter. As the pile mounted and grew heavier, Doc would begin to look back with increasing disapproval. When we finally decided the limit had been reached he was apt to get stubborn, especially if the load had to be pulled up an incline to get to the gate. Molly would lay into the traces with every ounce of her power. Doc would follow suit once or twice, but if the load did not begin to move easily, he would give up. Instead of moving forward he would start to back up, and with a vengeance, even threatening to foul the wagon wheels and overturn the whole mass. All too often we were obliged to pitch off part of the load to get any hay at all to the barn, and eventually we surrendered to his balkiness by building smaller loads, which of course prolonged haying to a marked degree.

In all truth, there was not enough work throughout the year for a team of horses. Haying required six weeks to two months; during the winter, manure had to be spread; and when snow filled the road, milk had to be taken down below where the milk truck could pass. They both loved that down-hill jaunt, gathering speed as we descended until they broke into full gallop, while I braced against the front of the wagon, sawing uselessly at the reins. Richard always wondered whether I would ever stop them; but when they reached the dock for the cans of milk, they would come to a sliding, stiff-legged halt that almost threw me right onto their backs. There they would snort and heave, toss their heads, switch their tails, proud as punch of their game. As I've already said, they put on the same act bringing a load of hay down from Hell's Acres. As the load pressed against them on the rather steep decline, they would walk faster and faster, change to a trot and then, as we reached the first sharp bend, pick up speed. By the time I steered them around the second abrupt turn into the lane leading to the barn, they again would launch into a gallop until they swept with a final surge up and onto the ramp between the hay mows. This was far more perilous than hauling milk, for riding on top of a shifting pile of hay requires an old sailor's balance, and if one of the horses had stumbled and fallen I suppose we all would have been badly injured, if not killed.

All in all, Molly and Doc were idle the greater part of every year. Even on pasture they required a small amount of grain and during the winter they consumed quantities of both hay and grain. They had to be harnessed and unharnessed, their stalls had to be cleaned, they themselves needed an occasional currying. In short they were more of an expense and bother than they were worth. Horses fitted picturesquely into my early farming scheme of slow work, a refusal to hurry, and a certain opposition to machinery; but I could no longer say that my team was entirely practical. Perforce, I debated buying a tractor though not with real gusto. Moreover, it was all too apparent that in winter I needed a vehicle that would get me on and off my hilltop through snow and over ice, not only to haul milk but to take me to town for weekly supplies when driving conditions were too much for the old Ford sedan, even equipped with chains. A jeep was the only solution. With a cab and a heater I would be almost as comfortable as in a car, a matter worth considering on the road but also not to be disparaged when spreading manure on cold, snowy days or in rain, especially in contrast to the unprotected seat of a tractor. Also a power take-off would mean that I could operate a mowing machine, even a buzz saw for a supply of fireplace wood. And ample power, at the turn of a switch instead of wrestling with a tangle of harness, would be available for hauling manure and hay or for whatever other job was called for. So a unanimous vote of one elected for the jeep and I bought one that had been used only three months. It has been invaluable. I sing its praises on every occasion. (An authentic indication of how much I travel during recent years is found on the speedometer. The original owner covered a lot of territory as an artificial inseminator and in three months had registered some 16,000 miles. In the ten years I have driven it, and for all field work and getting to town, the total is 34,000—18,000 miles in a decade. And the total on the Ford would be far less—if the speedometer worked.)

Haying, especially, promptly moved at a faster, smoother pace. There was little difficulty in holding the mower to the precise line that kept the knives clear of the preceding swath and just on the edge of the tall growth that was forming the succeeding one. If the knives fouled, a few feet in reverse usually cleared them. The single advantage of a tractor was that, upon arriving at the end of a course, it could make a sharp turn in reverse that swung the mower into position to start right off on the next. Because the jeep could not turn that quickly I was obliged to raise the cutter bar, swing around in as short a quarter-circle as possible and then drop the bar as I set off again. A side-delivery rake had been added as essential machinery, and with the jeep hitched on, it laid down long coiling windrows which the newly acquired loader picked up cleanly and fed onto the wagon, where Scoop tossed the hay about to build a solid load, in which he took inordinate pride. A newly windrowed field with its innumerable concentric lines, leading like a maze to the center, makes a handsome sight when the setting sun begins to cast the first shadows.

The slow jaunt to the barn was a pleasure, sure and predictable even on steep ground, the towering load swaying slightly but not dangerously on the turns, the wagon creaking its complaints beneath nearly two tons of hay. And a final spurt of power brought all of us up and onto the ramp for unloading without a hint of uncertainty.

With the acquiring of a manure spreader, my machinery needs were complete. Thereafter all farm labor was reduced to the attainable minimum of physical effort. I have never objected to loading manure in the barn, though I always resented taking a fork and throwing it off onto the fields, partly

51

because at best the result was uneven, big clods often being separated by open spaces, and also because the very idea of shoveling manure onto a wagon just to be obliged to pitch it off seemed like a miscarriage of justice. The spreader changed all that. Loading was good warming-up work that seemed to start the day off in promising fashion and required less than half an hour. Then into the jeep and off to a field where the spreader was put in gear, and away I moved, gazing back contentedly at the cloud of shredded dung behind me, returning to the soil a big share of the mineral and organic matter that had gone into hay and completing that ever-repeated cycle of the earth—birth, growth, decline and death. City folk are aware of it only as it affects humans, and with this narrow viewpoint they tend to register shock and sorrow when the cycle comes to its unavoidable end. When a man works with the earth, surrounded by wild life, linked closely to livestock, he glimpses the cycle on a vaster scale, sees it as the essential rhythm of generative force that has been operating for a few billion years and will continue for a few billion more in one form or another even if hydrogen bombs wipe out the human element. Thus death loses its calamitous aspect for death brings birth, not—for me at least—an afterlife in some celestial sphere, but here and now, and so attains a serene beauty that precludes grief. We live on detritus—how self-centered to bemoan a return to it!

Now for the third great change at High Meadows. Scoop, aided by scholarships, graduated from Harvard in 1952, decided on law and went to Columbia for three more years. Thus he was free during the summers up to 1955, and though he had not even a faint inclination toward farming, he was always eager to come to the hilltop, for which, after his fashion, he has as much affection as I have. With him, and with

Mary contributing her presence if not much labor, haying was not sheer drudgery. There were moments for laughter, for profane argument soon lost in the lightly stirring air and for compliments when one phase or another of the job was well done. We were, of course, glad when the last load had been stowed away in the barn, for Scoop and Mary then were free to take the jeep and swim at a nearby lake and I just to relax once again as a practitioner of what I style "horizontal farming," meaning that I am prone or supine, with a book or without, as much of the time as possible.

But when Scoop went to work with a New York law firm, I was left alone for the haying operation. All other farm work I had always taken as my responsibility and could handle without difficulty. All the fields had been plowed, by hired neighbors; I had harrowed and seeded them to a mixture of birdsfoot trefoil and timothy and then used them entirely for hay and pasture. With annual applications of manure, occasional fertilizer and lime, they promised to continue to yield into an indefinite future. But haying alone is a tough undertaking. Well before Scoop took on a life of his own I had mulled over the situation and found little that was pleasing in the general prospect. One thing seemed certain—I would have to have my hay baled and, with weather the ever uncertain threat, I would have to hire help to load bales and get them to the barn. Richard would do the baling, but the question of timing, of synchronizing his haying operation with mine, bothered me no end. Naturally, his work took precedence over mine, and delays were bound to occur, because of weather or the breaking down of machinery. The possibility that my hay, cut and windrowed, ready for the baler, might be obliged to lie in a field for several days while I fretted helplessly, watching the sky for storm portents, listening to weather broadcasts, was not exactly appealing, certain though I was that Richard would do his utmost to meet my schedule. Nevertheless, seeing no other solution, I tried it the following year.

After weeks of really exhausting, slogging labor, the hay was in the barn. A lot of it had had to be cut late and hay deteriorates rapidly in nutritive content once it has passed the early budding stage. I like, in fact, to cut hay as early in June as weather permits and hope that the last batch will not be too old by the time I get to it. But so does Richard. The result was that I had to put off cutting several times, a good share of hay got rained on either in windrows or in bales for lack of help, and I became increasing irritable and disgusted. Not that I blamed Richard. He gave of more than his best. It simply was impossible to mesh his job and mine to produce worthwhile results. I remember one section of East Meadow where the birdsfoot trefoil was especially luxuriant, actually so thick that when the mower sheared it off at the base it still stood upright as though the knives hadn't touched it. I raked it and waited. For three days it was a target for a boiling sun, dry and furnace hot. The second day I took the rake and turned over the heavy windrows. More sun and a breeze that almost audibly sucked moisture from leaves and stems. When Richard finally got free of mishaps and his own work and the baler came, the birdsfoot was toasted to a literal crisp. At the slightest touch of human fingers, to say nothing of that huge toothed maw of the baler, leaves turned to powder and fell to the ground. Only the tough stems remained as hay, utterly worthless hay, not worth putting in the barn.

That hay got properly cured and so did I, of any idea of haying alone. I did some figuring early the following spring, went to the bank, and explained my problem to the president, who has been a good friend ever since he laughed and took back a remark he made, when I bought the place, to the effect that I wouldn't last six months. He agreed to a loan of $800. I knew a winter supply of hay would cost approximately $1,000 and I had enough cash to make up that sum.

I vow I have been a more congenial person since that day. During the following years I got ahead of the game to such an extent that I had a thousand bucks in the bank when spring arrived and monthly payments on a loan became memories. Memories of that ilk are not displeasing.

Haying, even with the close approximation of ideal conditions that modern machinery provides, is hazardous. Commercial hay growers are so equipped—with big tractors, mowers, crushers (the latest implement that picks up hay the moment it is cut and passes it between rollers which press out most of the moisture, thus hastening the curing by as much as two days), side rakes, balers and big flatbed trucks, and with plenty of men on the job—that on a hot day they can cut early in the morning, crush the hay, rake it by noon and even start baling that evening. They can come very close to beating the weather, but not always. In this region a thunderstorm can hurtle out of the west almost before one can run to shelter. Their misfortune, however, is not mine. Rained-on hay is easily recognized by its brown color and texture. Dealers know better than to try to pass off such hay on farmers; so one is almost certain to find only good hay handled by dealers. Moreover, if I confer with a reliable dealer—and most dealers are reliable—before haying season begins, he will put aside the earliest cuttings until he has the forty-odd tons I require, and then deliver it in big trailer trucks capable of carrying sixteen tons and more. With two or three helpers the bales are unloaded and neatly stacked in the mows, and I do not lift a finger. One more note: by ordering hay early, with prompt payment in cash, one can bargain for a good price as the dealer is glad to move hay as rapidly as possible.

Hay has changed in kind and quality to a marked degree in recent years as feed for dairy cows. Twenty years ago timothy was an all-purpose grass that every farmer planted, sometimes mixed with clover. Timothy is still the base for mixed hays because it is hardy and fast-growing and provides a lot of bulk. Alfalfa, however, has now become the roughage that most dairy farmers prefer, even demand. In a good season, alfalfa can be cut three, even four times, though as a rule two big cuttings are the average in these parts. The first cutting always contains a sizable proportion of weeds but later cuttings are pure alfalfa and, cut at the right moment and properly cured, it does make beautiful hay. Nevertheless, it is expensive, up to $35 and $40 a ton, even higher in late winter when the farmer's hay supply may be running low, and I am not at all persuaded that it is worth it. Being a legume it has a high protein content; and, when it is supplemented by a feed of grains mixed with oils, molasses, etc., the cow gets a rich ration that to my mind leads to digestive troubles. I prefer a mixed hay, timothy and alfalfa, timothy and birdsfoot trefoil (also a legume and slowly becoming popular), which can be fed generously without risk and which the cows clean up with gusto. Thus the cow's bodily sustenance is amply provided for, and mixed grain is relied upon as the principal milk maker. Tests have shown that timothy if cut before the flowering stage when the green head is just emerging from the surrounding leaf, or "boot," is almost as high in protein as alfalfa. Cut in late July, even in August, which was customary not long ago, it is like straw. But commercial growers no longer cut it so early. Why? Because horses are in greatly reduced numbers compared with a decade or more ago. Horse owners demanded young, fine hay and they got it. Now the growers cut timothy when it is older and has more bulk, thus adding to total tonnage.

All in all my new system is much to my liking. The hay is far superior to what my average was bound to be over a long haying period, it has not been rained on, it is well cured so that only rarely do I encounter a moldy bale, and I am relieved of all the work. Not only the work but the worry, the tension that develops gradually throughout the haying season, partly because of inevitable mechanical breakdowns, seemingly always at the most critical moments when "Hurry, Hurry" is an ever-present goad, but mainly because of weather. Truly experienced farmers, raised on farms and with a lifetime of accepting the quirks and whims of nature, possess a mentality I have given up hope of ever achieving. Richard, for example, pushes ahead with his haying, unmindful of weather forecasts, not even greatly concerned by lowering skies that could produce a downpour within an hour. Not until the first raindrops fall does he increase his tempo, and he takes off for the barn only when he decides that he is caught in more than a light sprinkle. Frequently, to my envy and even irritation, he is the winner. Rain does not develop, the few drops have done no damage and he is several hours ahead toward completing the job. I have asked him how he dares to defy all the omens of bad weather, how he can bring himself to cutting hay when there is virtual certainty that it will get rained on. Without looking up or interrupting whatever tinkering job he is engaged with, he says, "I have a lot of work that must be done over the summer. If I get behind in haying, then I'm behind with everything else and some work just doesn't get finished. If I waited for good weather I'd never get through haying. So I keep going, taking a chance."

Such equanimity is beyond me. I stew in indecision, persuading myself it will rain if I do cut hay, the next minute persuading myself it will clear if I don't cut. I don't want to talk, I resent suggestions. I insist on wallowing in my black mood, alone. Buying hay offered a sure escape from this kind of torture that got me precisely nowhere, and this factor played as much of a part in the final vote as the more practical benefits. The cost in money seemed negligible.

That cash outlay, moreover, I discovered to my pleasure, was noticeably reduced by a more consistent flow of milk from the cows during the winters and a near flood of milk in May and June when the cows were positively sated with lush pasture. A couple of hours of browsing stuffed even their capacious paunches. The rest of the day or night they spent in a relaxed, contented stupor, interrupted only occasionally by rumbling belches, and cuds continued their rhythm of rising for indolent chewing and descending for more of the digestive process. The cows were at peace and so was I.

4.

SUCH were the three major changes that added in large measure to the good life at High Meadows, which now was an extremely close approximation of what life could be, indeed should be if this earthly existence is to be more than a succession of trials and tribulations. Without the haying chore I still had enough work to keep physically fit, though I did acquire a few extra pounds around the belt line, together with a generous allotment of leisure which never led to a single moment of monotony or boredom. There is so much to be done with spare time in the country; new interests are forever cropping up to replace or augment the old. Not that interests, new and old, are not offered by the city. For years I was very much an urbanite, finding excitement and amusement on any prolonged stroll along the pavements of any section of a city. But over the years people increased in numbers until one was obliged to concentrate on avoiding humans and automobiles instead of contemplating a handsome structure or whatever of the unusual caught the eye. Pavements seemed to grow harder, noise and dust became annoying.

My 155 acres offer solitude, yielding earth underfoot, and silence insofar as man- or machine-made noises are involved—though, of course, the woods are never completely silent. If I wish to turn over a stone to inspect what may be under it, I can hunker down and spend an hour in that one spot, undisturbed, rapt in my observations and imaginings. I find an endless fascination while sitting on a stump or fallen bole deep in the woods, waiting for my motionless presence to be accepted by all the hidden life around me until a woodpecker ventures into view seeking food; a gray squirrel moves from behind the branch that conceals him and chatters both a challenge and a warning before making a long leap into the next tree. The leaves at my feet begin to stir; beetles, crickets, a great array of insects proceed about their innumerable affairs; a fat and striking black-and-yellow spider mends the web that has been rent by the fly it has just finished devouring. I lack the patience of the born naturalist; I could never be a Fabre so absorbed by a few wasps that time has no meaning, but I relish the privilege, however short-lived, of emulating him until I am distracted. I can be supremely happy absorbing sunshine in a comfortable chair on the terrace, the mind in very low gear, almost but not quite empty, or in an equally comfortable chair before the fireplace while the winter wind crashes savagely against the house. Being alone is in no way a form of punishment for me. I welcome it. But don't get me wrong. Tomorrow I will be just as pleased when several friends arrive and we gather round a table eating and drinking, laughing and talking for hours while I winnow from incessant conversation information about friends and happenings in a variety of places, in Europe and here.

So I achieve a very satisfying balance between solitude and cameraderie, with animals taking over the latter role in exemplary fashion any time I am aware of a dearth of human companionship—even to the point where I question whether I should permit myself to become deeply involved in such friendship, establish a form of devotion for an animal with the uncontradictable knowledge that it must come to an end. I have said that I regard death as one of four phases in nature's cycle; and because it is just as inevitable as the other phases, birth, growth and decline, it should be accorded no greater importance than the others. Birth follows death and so death achieves a glory or beauty of its own that transcends grief, the primitive reaction that should be superseded by modern intelligence and reason. I hold firmly with that when humans are concerned, but my attitude changes with animals and I find this difficult to explain.

It appears to relate to the lack of reasoning power in animals. They do not have the faculty for correlating the various elements that combine to cut short a relationship, an affection, that has endured for years to the mutual benefit of the animal and me. It has become dependent on me, as no adult human can, looking to me for its entire well-being, yet in no way can I explain to it the long-determined series of events which compel separation. This barrier is most acutely sensed with cows, those intimate friends with whom I have lived inseparably these many years. I was away from them exactly three days in more than thirteen years. But I am also distinctly aware of the barrier with other animals, though in varying degrees on a descending graph until I reach bottom with rabbits and chickens.

Now I like rabbit meat, wild or tame. It is delicate, of excellent flavor and as fully adaptable in the hands of an imaginative cook as chicken. At one stage when we were living in the lovely Chevreuse Valley outside of Paris, I took some time off from newspaper work to try some writing of my own. We were on a tight budget so that, when an ardent hunter or a neighbor took to quietly hanging a rabbit on our door early every morning, the surplus of his daily bag as well as testimony to his skill, we were delighted. We ate rabbit cooked in every possible way, with or without wine, with all congealed blood extractable to make a civet, stewed, fried, baked. And when we exhausted the variations, I made a *paté*, which on a warm midday, with a jug of wine and crusty bread under an appletree, comprised a delicious lunch. Fortunately the hunting season ended while we were still able to eat rabbit with moderate though dwindling gusto.

So not long after arriving at High Meadows I invested in two does and a buck of the New Zealand White breed, big, handsome, pure white and pink-eyed specimens. They were comfortably housed in one of those iron frame and heavy wire mesh pens for laying hens, with three tiers of two compartments each. Soon, believing the book, I told myself I would need another battery of six compartments. Like everyone else I was familiar with the storied reproductive powers of the rabbit, rivaled apparently only by the mink. Other than feeding them, my major duty was to note by various outward and unmistakable signs when a doe was in heat, or rut, and then solicitously introduce a buck into her cage. But Nature manages to be more complex than that. The wooing process is a fairly fixed ritual. Perhaps in the wild state, several suitors are part of the ritual, permitting the amorous but coy doe to select her amorous but never bashful mate.

Be that as it may, I hardly qualified as a successful rabbit breeder. In the main, my efforts to assure that Nature's urge would be consummated resulted in frantic pursuits within the cage, hysterical assaults against the bars, winding up in a furious battle of the sexes, with the doe coming out on top, which was no help, until the buck retired to a corner, temporarily defeated and humiliated. The book advised holding the recalcitrant doe but on the rare occasions when I did manage to anchor her for as much as five minutes, usually getting bitten or clawed, the buck gave every evidence of resenting my interference and huffily remained at a distance. In my opinion my sporadic successes came only when the doe came to such a stage of physical fatigue that she could do nothing else but submit to her wooer, if by that time his ardency, too, had not become gelid.

However, by accident or because Nature will not be thwarted, success would be signaled by the increasing girth of the doe and a litter of young would be born, four or five, even six. Then they began to disappear, one by one, by day or by night—sometimes in the very young, helpless and extremely nude state; sometimes after they had sprouted fur and were able to move about. It was very odd and annoying. I solved that mystery by sheer chance when I arrived unexpectedly in the shed one day and found Pooch, our wily seven-toed cat, clinging to the outside of the cage where a doe had her nest of progeny. Pooch vanished in a rush but it was easy to complete the picture. She would climb to the cage where her snarling face scared the doe out of her wits so that she cowered as far away as possible while Pooch fished into the corner nest with one paw armed with fishhooks and extracted a light but delectable repast. I balked that kind of rapine by attaching wire screening to the side of the cage. She outsmarted me once again when I put a pregnant doe in a small chickenhouse, with a door that could be closed tight and two windows which I left partly open at the top because of midsummer heat. With Pooch in mind I nailed old window screens on the outside. They were too short, but I assured myself that Pooch would never even discover the narrow aperture, to say nothing of squeezing through it. Pooch, I learned, was never to be underestimated. She spread carnage through the shack in one night—cleaned up the entire litter of quarter-grown bunnies.

Decimation of my infrequent rabbit offspring nevertheless continued after Pooch bowed to defeat. Death would intervene in one of several forms—the young getting stepped on, sickness, malnutrition, etc. At no time did all six compartments get filled. Of course, we had rabbit to eat from time to time, yet such festive meals were so widely spaced during a year that we had no reason to fear tiring of such diet. When my rabbitry was reduced to a buck and a doe that was indomitably disposed to spinsterhood, I threw in my rabbit-fur hat. We ate the one and then the other.

I certainly did not relish killing a rabbit when one was both available and voted for as a meal. That was merely my aversion to killing animals in general. I used to go forth every autumn, find a rock to sit on, close to a few hickory trees, and wait for a gray squirrel to come within range, because I like squirrel fried or as a major component in a real Brunswick stew. But even an annual craving for such a dish has not sufficed in recent years to urge me out with a shotgun. I have more amusement in seeing how well I can camouflage my presence so that a squirrel or a grouse or even a pheasant will come to within a few yards of me until a sense of danger brings the head up and flight follows, a swift dash to the other side of a tree or a rocketing charge toward undergrowth and a zigzag course to safety. With rabbits, however, I was able to be completely impersonal. There was no bond of affection between us. I found them invariably nervous, scary and rather brainless as individuals. I could stroke them, even pick them up without marked objection, but always they seemed to submit out of dumb acquiescence to a power beyond their understanding rather than because they knew me and had confidence in me.

The same attitude holds true when I deal with chickens. During the early years I kept a dozen or so hens, for eggs and, as each passed the laying age, for dishes of rich stewed chicken, *arroz con pollo, poule au pot* and so forth. At least there were no mating problems, roosters being banned. But chickens are dirty, fidgety, totally lacking in character or appeal, yet requiring more care than my interest in them warranted. I was glad to settle down to buying fresh eggs from a neighbor and broilers, fryers or stewers at the market, for which they were mass produced, well fed and at a price below my cost for raising them. On a huge scale, literally thousands upon thousands of birds, there is unquestionably a profit in the business; but when I buy a fryer at approximately thirty cents a pound retail, I know that any farmer who hoped to make a little money on the side with five hundred to a thousand birds, must have been shocked when he compared the cost to him and the wholesale price he received. In any case, I never was aware of much compunction when the moment came to lay a chicken neck on the block and end it all with an axe stroke.

Now to move up on this escalator of affection for barnyard fauna, we come to pigs. On first thought the pig is hardly endowed with any of the gifts that make for lovableness. All pigs look alike except for color variations, and they seem to act alike, clumsy, snuffling, grunting creatures interested only in food and sleep. Their small, deep-set eyes are suspicious of all mankind except when a pail of slops is in evidence, and they are startled into high-gear movement by anything unexpected. Yet when one deals with just one or two porkers, from weanlings to maturity, they show different traits that distinguish one from the other and emanate something which certainly is not charm but does possess a curious appeal. Undoubted this derives from the fact that they are unconscious comics, and more intelligent than appearance indicates.

One pair I bought in the early years became known as Sodom and Gomorrah, for the only reason, as I recall, that the names are never separated just as the two little pigs were always together. I built a solid pen of planks and posts, one corner of which was formed by a small chickenhouse to which S and G could retire out of the sun. But one side of the pen was a stone wall and that was my error. When half-grown and as persistently active as any animal in existence, they developed the ability of a mountain goat, finding plenty of footholds in the stacked stones to permit them to scramble perpendicularly for nearly four feet, hike themselves to the top amid loud squeals and take off with a mighty leap into the inviting open spaces. I was annoyed at first but soon learned that they had no desire to stray very far and that they would come to the pen in a hurtling, noisy rush when I called them for evening food. Moreover, they remained there for the night. During the day they stayed in the small meadow by the house, side by side and, as though activated by jet propulsion, lunging ahead, leaping aside, with the perfect timing of a vaudeville team—real "hoofers" I might say, going through a well rehearsed dance—and all for no reason and to no special purpose. Any time I felt the need to laugh, which was frequent during the first years, I could perch on the stone wall and watch Sodom and Gomorrah in their silly capers and get my fill.

I bought the young pigs with the long cherished intention of smoking my own hams and bacons—no more pallid, watery commercial products for me. Thus, when they attained 200 pounds in weight I had to face the problem of slaughter, scalding, scraping and butchering, the several orthodox steps described in detail in the book and suddenly assuming dreadful proportions. I weakened rapidly, consulted with a carpenter friend who also raised pigs for his own use, and appointed him executioner and commander-in-chief of the entire job. He accepted with one provision: the month was November, the weather was raw and cold, so a supply of hard cider would be essential to ward off inflammations and congestions from exposure. Not only did that strike me as reasonable; I realized that I would need a little fortifying just to get through the whole affair.

Having arrived one morning with his pickup truck and a .22 rifle, Firmin dispatched the two pigs while I found work to do in the barn. Then we loaded the carcasses into the truck and took off for his place, where he had a huge cauldron of water heating and a pal waiting, our Ganymede for the rest of the day. I have no great liking for hard cider; but I downed a glassful of it at once for I had abruptly come out of my dream of luscious smoked hams and home-cured bacon to realize how much I would miss Sodom and Gomorrah, their clownish antics, the way they had come to delight in having their floppy ears scratched. Only because I was immediately assigned jobs to do did I ease regret out of my mind. My two lowly pigs had come to have identities, personalities; they had become more a part of my daily life than rabbits or chickens; their departure would leave a bit of vacuum. On the other hand, I persuaded myself, they could never be classed as pets; they were the proper age and weight; the only thing to do was butcher them. I drank another glass of hard cider and went to my work.

Despite frequent jug passing, the whole job moved along steadily. The carcasses were shaved to a baby-pink hue and split in two, and one was cut into suitable pieces. The other had been promised to the local butcher and I made a small profit on it. When I studied the mound of fresh pork resulting from the dismemberment of one pig, I decided to be over-generous in sharing it with Firmin and his pal. I couldn't possibly cope with so much, even if I ate pork every day, which I had no intention of doing. So I took the hams and bacon and a sizable chunk of one loin, since the latter also could be smoked if necessary. The rest I left to the butchers. In the midst of so much pork, I lost all desire to make the various concoctions I had long contemplated—head cheese, scrapple, the *boudin* or blood sausage I had liked so much in France, even the plain pork sausage and lard I had planned to render, with the resultant cracklin's. My tastebuds were beyond titillation; a long winter with such a store of delectables offered no temptation. I had had enough.

Because the hams and bacon turned out to be quite acceptable, even slightly better in my somewhat partial opinion than "boughten," the urge revived the following spring and I bought one infant porker. That was Billy Budd. He was even more fun than Sodom and Gomorrah and almost a pet, following me about almost like a dog, coming up onto the porch frequently though departing in a tremendous clatter when shooed away. The thought of killing him became increasingly unpleasant as the summer ended. I insisted to myself that this was ridiculous, that a pig is a pig, a dumb beast whose destiny is fulfilled when it is transmuted into good food. With no little effort I finally evolved a state of mind that permitted me to kill Billy Budd. With Scoop, we went through the entire process I had learned the year before, though awkwardly and requiring much more time. I kept calling myself a damned fool throughout the task, and eventually the final chunk was carved. I did make head cheese, I did make a crockful of excellent sausage, and again I wilted. Neighbors were surprised to receive some free cuts of pork; I cured and smoked hams and bacon, and called it quits. I have never raised a pig since and never will. I had lots of other chores to attend to.

Let us move up a little higher on the steps. Parting with the horses did not prove to be the emotional trial I had anticipated at an earlier time. Once I had decided, with logic and evidence preponderantly in support, that a jeep was more practical than my team, I had a kind of built-in lenitive that diluted sentiment. My whilom vow to keep at least Molly until she succumbed to old age, had the ring of something I might have read in tales like *Black Beauty*. I was not going to make Molly happier, so I reasoned, by keeping her until her teeth were gone and her ribs started to show through her sleek hide, until she became unsteady on her legs. She was still in good health; she had demonstrated her gallant spirit through years of toil—why not bring quick death before the remnants of her prime were certain to fade? I turned to Anatole France's eulogy and envy of the butterfly, which died in its full-blown glory while mounting toward the sun in pursuit of love. Molly was no Pegasus but she was aware of my affection for her— declare, then, that her time had come. Doc, of course, was easier to count off. He simply was not the type to rouse a feeling of attachment. Too many memories of his numerous failings intervened for that.

Separation came at a moment when there was ample distraction to take my mind off horses. Not long before I had discussed the matter with a local dealer, without making a final decision. He had agreed to sell them for slaughter, not for work, a stipulation I insisted on and which presented no difficulty since work horses were in so reduced demand that they brought the same price for one as for the other purpose. And in the midst of a hilarious dinner, a dozen of us gathered about a table outdoors feasting on clams steamed in white wine and lobsters shipped alive from Maine, all with much wine bibbing, the dealer drove up. I excused myself, laughing from the gay chatter, and with no bother about bargaining asked what he would give for the team. They were close by in pasture, he looked them over and named a sum that I hardly listened to, I agreed, he paid me, and because the swirl of talk and cries from the other side of the house was more than audible, I hardly had to announce that I had guests and would leave the loading to him. I was back at table in five minutes and stayed there until long after dark. Not until the following morning did I discover the money in my pocket and realize that the horses were gone—by which time, obviously, regrets were too late and already minuscule.

Cats do not really rate inclusion in this list of farm animals. We have barn cats and have never attempted to bring a kitten into the house as a permanent dweller. Nevertheless the barn cats are pets and are frequently ensconced near the kitchen door, ever ready for a tidbit that might be tossed to them but seldom is, because I try to be firm in my conviction that barn cats have one primary duty—to keep the barn free of mice and rats. There they get milk every morning and evening and, in my opinion, should forage for the balance of their provender. But Mary thwarts me by surreptitiously handing out snacks in my absence. She argues, and with feminine rationalization to which I bow, that there are always scraps to be rid of. So we have compromised. The cats get one meal a day at the house, at which I whoop in derision but to no avail.

I admire cats. They are the most self-centered, blatantly selfish quadrupeds on this earth. They are masters of mendicancy. They are the most arrant frauds imaginable. They are feline prostitutes selling their gifts to the highest bidder. And they take immense pride in their charlatanry. Such deserve admiration. There is a singleness of purpose therein that makes me envious, particularly because always they are the winner, with a smug, chop-licking, paw-polishing air of triumph that is a perfect blend of the diabolical and the godly. The Egyptians were right to deify them.

Admiration leads to a degree of affection, especially if one is in frequent contact with a cat. I confess to affection for our cats, reassuring myself that I can because I see through their humbug all too clearly. So we get along fine.

Pooch was our first cat. The day I moved in, she arrived from the farm below and elected to stay. I welcomed her, for otherwise Molly was the only form of domestic life to keep me company. Pooch was big, with black stripes on gray, and was unique to me because she had seven toes forward and five aft, more than the usual cat quota though the seventh toes were hardly more than claws. Her front feet looked like miniature boxing gloves and, as I learned later, were lethal weapons for snaring birds and animals up to the size of gray squirrels. A great hunter and, for the most part, quite content to hold rodent life in the barn to a minimum and then range the lanes and meadows for supplementary prey, she asked for little petting, resented it strenuously if she was picked up for fondling. She turned to me only when her kittens were weaned, which happened with dismaying regularity three times a year. From some secret hideaway in the barn she would emerge with four or five frolicking, high-tailed offspring, guide them with military discipline to the milk pan by the milkhouse and proudly bequeath them to me. From then on, the maternal spirit waned rapidly and she was free to resume her carefree life. This meant also that, unless I decided to run a cat farm, I had to get rid of them. A few I did succeed in giving away over the years, for those of her kittens that had seven toes were an oddity, a kind of collector's item. The others had to be drowned or, if too elusive to be caught, killed with the shotgun.

Either procedure I disliked intensely. I discovered I could accomplish it only by transferring my dislike for the job itself to the kittens. Not until I had worked up an actual hatred for the kittens as sources of repeated misery for me was I able to grab one while it lapped milk, then thrust it into a bag and into a waiting pail of water. I haven't changed in all these years. It's the one task I loath absolutely, and cannot avoid.

Pooch died of old age and I was touched by the powerful urge that defied weakness and brought her to the barn, to die at home. She had been showing signs of age for several months. Her coat had lost its smoothness and luster, her movements were slower, even her fine yellow eyes seemed to be dulling. I didn't see her for a couple of days, then found her on the barn floor one morning, flat on her belly, with dirt in her fur, still trying to haul herself forward, one leg at a time, to her customary bed by the calf pen. Her eyes opened wider when I talked to her as though she now was certain she was home. I lifted her onto an empty feed bag, noticing that the fur on her legs had been worn away to bare hide but also that there was no wound or injury. Very plainly, strength had started to drain from her while she was some distance away, leaving mostly will power to consummate the long drag over dirt and stones and bring her back to where she belonged. That she had achieved, at great cost. I looked at her a few minutes later and she was dead.

The Pooch dynasty has continued unbroken down to the present, with the heraldic emblem of seven toes as guarantee of legitimacy, though legitimacy in the cat realm is less restrictive than in the human code. The present incumbents are Snazzy, Pooch's many time great-granddaughter, and Snazzy's son, Butch. It is here that legitimacy in our concept is loosely applied; for by all the feline signs with which I have become familiar, Snazzy's next batch of kittens will be products of incest. Butch is a big animal and thus far he seems to have compelled his ma's suitors from around the countryside to limit their amorous proclivities to other farms.

Snazzy is every bit the equal of her distant ancestor as a hunter, but she has been spoiled to the extent that she insists on one meal a day at the house though she may be bulging from a gluttonous banquet of a whole young rabbit or a gray squirrel. Handsomer than Pooch, with black and tawny markings on dark gray, with glowing yellow eyes, she makes full use of this appeal along with unlimited patience in wearing down one's resistance. When she decides a meal should be forthcoming, if only because she feels too indolent to hunt, she stretches out close to the door and waits, and waits, making no sound but alert to every move within, starting up if one of us approaches the door to make sure she is seen, sinking back if nothing happens. She moves away if menacing motions are made but she is back in the same spot minutes later. This is begging in its highest form as an art. It is irresistible. And she knows it. Firm resolves begin to disintegrate, despair mounts and finally surrender is unconditional. Food is put on a plate and given to her while she purrs in triumph. Chalk up another victory over the vulnerable human.

From all I have been able to observe, Butch has never caught a thing. He is far too indolent for the chase. When he is absent it is for one of two reasons or, if he is lucky, a combination of the two. He is making his rounds as a lordly male seeking concubines or he is raiding cat dishes set out at nearby farms. Reports have it that he knows the hour when these dishes are replenished and appears precisely then to enjoy his share as the uninvited guest. He is so confident he will get the living the world owes him that he is laughable.

Yet I wouldn't be without cats, though not more than two at a time. They are valuable in the barn and they are fascinating to study. Nevertheless, I would look upon them with a more benign eye if I could reduce kitten production to one a year—not one litter, just one kitten.

Also there is the cruelty of cats. I don't get upset by the knowledge that some animals are predators, even that some kill wantonly when hunger no longer is a driving force which, by Nature's logic, justifies the killing. Then they kill out of madness, a mounting lust that gets out of all control. They do not, however, so far as I am aware, deliberately torture their victims. And that is what a cat does with a revolting refinement of cruelty which at times enrages me to such a point that I vow I will get rid of them all. Pooch was no exception; Snazzy engages in it with still greater zest, inordinately proud of her power over her small captive, inviting lavish praise if she has an audience. With a precisely controlled bite along the spine of a chipmunk, which does not even break the skin, she inflicts a partial paralysis, permitting the chipmunk to move about, fully conscious but unable to attain sufficient speed to escape. The hope of reaching shelter and safety is all too evident in its bright eyes as it struggles here and there; but just as victory seems near, Snazzy leaps in and gently cuffs it back into the open, then rolls over in ecstasy while watching the animal renew its fruitless efforts. It is totally unfair, the chipmunk has no chance, yet Snazzy will prolong her game for five or ten minutes, until fatigue reduces the victim to a small heap of quivering fur. Then Snazzy steps in and devours it, to the last hair.

Even more repulsive it is when she brings a crippled chipmunk or mouse to her kittens, which come tumbling forth at her call. The first one gets the prize; and though it may be its first encounter with a living animal, instinct asserts itself and the kitten plays the game with the same skill as its mother, with equal gusto, with equal lack of pity. Little wonder I cheer the swallows when several of them catch Snazzy in the open and stage their dive-bombing attacks, swooping down at top speed and with shrill cries, one hot after the other, to within inches of her, causing her to duck her head and flatten out on the ground until she breaks and runs. The swallows, of course, never strike her, but there is a pent-up fury in their assault for which she has no liking.

With the exception of Pooch, the cats that have resided at High Meadows have never attained old age and have disappeared without intervention by me. Passing cars certainly take their toll, and I suppose roaming dogs or wild animals such as fox or mink, might account for others. In any event they have vanished and I have been aware of it only after several days of absence. And since they never were counted as real pets, the parting has been without pangs for me. Now, however, we come to dogs and the chances for heartbreak are measurably increased.

There has been just one dog at High Meadows and he will have no successor. I am determined on that. Susquie was six weeks old when he was presented to me by a friend. A fat, clumsy, tawny puppy, half German Shepherd, half Dobermann Pinscher, he grew into a handsome animal, weighing some eighty pounds, full of spirit, taking part in every outdoor activity, delighting in the horses, playing with but never plaguing the cows. He learned that chickens and cats were not in his province but that woodchucks were; and he truly was death on the latter pests, which dig holes in the fields and pile up mounds of dirt and stones which can cause a horse to break a leg or the mower knives to foul repeatedly. He was quiet in the house but a whirlwind of energy outdoors, playing with Scoop until exhausted, friendly with everybody, all in all a fine specimen of farm dog.

He took special joy in haying, jumping at the horses and snapping his teeth, to which they paid no attention, ripping off in quest of a woodchuck and finally, when a load of hay was completed, scrambling to the top and barking his delight in life. In the barn, where the hay was unloaded with a big fork that dropped it into one of the mows, he leaped about in a frenzy of excitement when the big heap of hay descended on him, burying him until he managed to come surging to the top as though it were a wave of water. We enjoyed all this as much as he did; he typified the happy farm dog, completely free, one of us when we worked, stretched out by the house when work was over with one ear cocked for any sound that might indicate another rousing game was about to start. We adored him and he returned affection in every possible canine way.

Problems arose for the very simple reason that he had too much idle time for his exuberant nature. Particularly when haying ended, we had no regular work in the fields and Susquie was inevitably left to himself. After lolling about the house, waiting for excitement and finding none, he was unable to restrain his excess of energy and took off in pursuit of woodchucks. Then he began to roam the woods, chasing squirrels and rabbits; then he explored in wider circles—he came to roads with cars hurrying by, to farms with other dogs, other animals, other people. What else could be expected?

We paid little attention to his absence as he always returned after a few hours. And even if I had thought of chaining him near the barn I doubt if I would have done so, for that would have struck me as punishment, which he did not deserve and could not understand. I would have balked strenuously at such evident cruelty. Yet the upshot should have been obvious to us. One day an enraged neighbor, whom I knew very slightly and who lived some three miles away back in the valley, drove up and announced that Susquie had raided an outdoor rabbit pen containing his children's pets and killed one. I expressed my regrets, adding that nothing like it had ever happened before, offered to buy another bunny, finally calmed him down and went to get Susquie. I tied him up for two days, trusting he would realize his guilt, understand why he was being punished. Certainly he did not like it; I relented and turned him loose.

The problem, however, had not been solved. Sheer boredom revived the urge to wander, and he took to going to the more traveled road below and chasing cars. Inevitably he became a trifle too careless and was hit a glancing blow. He came back with a flap of skin nearly the size of my hand dangling along one hind leg. It wasn't a serious injury and we left Susquie to take care of it as a lesson to him. Perhaps it was a lesson for the two weeks it took him to lick the wound until it was completely healed and the hair growing back, but not much longer.

The following year during haying, with Susquie cavorting as usual in the hay as it was unloaded, Mary remarked that the dog was rubbing his eyes frequently and that they looked slightly grayish. Examination showed what looked like a thin film gathering over one eye. Closer observation revealed that sight in that eye was somewhat impaired. We took Susquie to the small animal clinic at Cornell University, where specialists verified our finding and advised leaving him for treatment. Ten days later we returned for him. The doctor said the eye was better after removal of the film, but they were not at all optimistic that the growth would not return. Their diagnosis was that dust and pollen from the hay was the cause. Well, we kept Susquie out of the hay, kept him with us all the time, but the growth did come back, a form of cataract, and the other eye became affected. We went to the clinic again and I asked the doctor for his frank opinion. It was, as I had already decided, that he could do nothing more, that Susquie would soon be blind. None of us could bear the thought of a blind Susquie, blundering about the house, unable to race about the fields with all his splendid energy. There would be no kindness in keeping him alive for such a semi-existence. So we hugged him, kissed him farewell and left him to be destroyed, the finest dog I ever owned.

Admittedly, blindness from such a cause is most unusual. I

never have heard of another case in the region, where other dogs surely romp in hay occasionally. But there were other factors that had become burdensome to us and I decided with unalterable finality that, as I have said, I would never have another dog at High Meadows. More, I am of the firm opinion that farm dogs no longer have the place they once enjoyed and that the city dog is a much happier animal, circumscribed though his life is and contradictory to all dog instincts. With no knowledge of fields and woods, of hopping and running animals inviting him to pursuit, of enticing scents and odors prodding his instincts, he adapts well to the narrow routine of apartment life and all in all is a contented dog. Companionship, affection and proper care are all he needs to fill out his succession of days and years.

Today's farm dog faces a radically different situation. Not many years ago he was an integral part of farm life. He herded cows, to and from the barn, horses likewise; he protected the chickens from marauders, just as he kept guard on the house. And he was the playmate for the children in their early years. In other words he had fixed duties and in their performance he understood his usefulness, the purpose of his life. All this has changed. Dairy farmers prefer to fetch their high-producing cows themselves, to avoid excitement and nervousness. Barnyard fowl are no longer common to every farm and, when they are kept, the danger from predatory intruders is hardly worth considering. Young children may enjoy a dog for a time; but soon they are riding in cars, away from the farm just as their mother is whenever possible, while the farmer works with machinery that holds no attraction for a dog. Without companionship, with no duties demanded of him, the dog inevitably goes in quest of distraction, an escape from boredom. And he gets into trouble, especially when he joins with others in the same dilemma and runs in a pack. Otherwise he must be chained. Either way is evil. If the dog is man's best friend, man would do well to return that friendship by leaving dogs to city-dwellers.

5.

A MACABRE OVERTONE becomes evident in the foregoing presentation of a farmer and his animals. It is not in the least exaggerated. Animals must be parted with, death will intervene, usually foreseen, also without warning. Of necessity one becomes inured to these unwelcome disturbances in the pastoral calm that had been envisioned but never completely won. The nagging uncertainty persists that what is recognized as unavoidable might have been avoided. And by the time one upset has blurred in memory, another is not long in intruding. And how painfully true it is with cows.

For the most part, dairy farmers regard milk production as a business. They are right. Considered strictly as a business the whole undertaking becomes more impersonal. Cows are looked upon as machines to be used until they wear out. Then they are discarded, new machines take their place and the business continues without interruption. No personal bond develops between man and cow, no more than between man and a smoothly functioning machine. As a responsible dairyman, he allots the same care to cows as he does to his machines to assure getting full usage, and the relationship ends there. If a cow proves to be a disappointment he takes the setback in stride as he does when a machine breaks down, cussing loudly in each instance but getting right on with his business.

Dairying came to me as an unexpected form of livelihood wherein cows were so decidedly the key factors that they took on an aspect removing them completely from the "sordid realm of business." They were far too special to be counted as machines. And when I became enamored of several in my herd that were docile and understanding despite my clumsiness, I became outright devoted to them. I still am, unwaveringly. But I have learned that by permitting affection to become so strong I likewise expose myself to more heartbreaks, keener disappointments. When a cow I have raised from birth proves to be a washout I am involved in tragedy with a strong sense of guilt that I was at fault, not the cow. When a cow I have raised passes her prime, falls off in milk and must be disposed of, I get into a sentimental stew that means weeks of delay before I can decide to summon a cattle dealer. That's not the way to run a business but it seems to be my way of gaining a livelihood. Moreover, I know a few other dairy farmers who get as ensnared by their cows as I do, which provides moral support, if and when needed.

So a pox on business, on money-making as an exalted goal. Years of my kind of dairying have not produced ulcers. I had no ambition for wealth when I came to High Meadows. But a livelihood has been attained as well as a way of life that is greatly to my liking. I owe it to my cows. Gloss over the heartbreaks, then, sweep the discouragements under the rug and forget them at least for the moment. The rewards manage to balance the reverses and they are more pleasing to consider. How long will this be true? I can only hazard a guess and in a case such as mine it is: not for long.

This is a time of crises. Put a finger anywhere on a world map and you will find trouble of one kind or another. In almost every instance food deficiencies are the basis. Only in recent years have Americans become a little more than vaguely aware that tens of millions of humans are victims of malnutrition, all too frequently to the point of starvation. Political and national stability depend upon full stomachs, for hunger spawns desperation, desperation explodes into revolution. New governments take over, land reforms are carried out and progress is made toward producing more food for the population. Meanwhile the steady, ever-mounting increase in population not only keeps pace with increased production, but surpasses it with gathering momentum.

In the United States, men in public life speak very nearly in unison and with pride of our population growth—more than 200,000,000 by 1970 and the figure growing phenomenally thereafter, decade by decade. Now this is no longer pioneer country. There are no more vast prairies or rich valleys to explore. On the contrary we are now in two straitjackets—one our natural borders; the other the amount of arable land that can be put into production. Even an expansion of irrigated land, the transformation of remaining desert, has reached very nearly its limit because of our ever-diminishing water supply by comparison with our ever-expanding demands. Extreme as it may at first appear, the possibility of soil exhaustion must be considered. Surveys reveal just how many natural phosphates remain in the world. Phosphates are a prime ingredient in fertilizer, in maintaining soil fertility. That supply won't run out next year, but eventually it will. Soon afterward we may all be living on a decidedly monotonous diet of algae, which can be produced in unlimited quantities in the oceans. Hence, I am not predicting imminent starvation. Rather, my point for the immediate future is the following. As population grows, the demands on agricultural production, in this country alone, must increase. Today's bemoaning of crop surpluses will change to envious recollections of plenitude. Abetted by all that scientific research can provide—new seeds, new methods, more efficient machinery—our cultivated land will be hard pressed to fill all those new stomachs.

The one solution, obviously, is increasing organization. Farming will of necessity have to be transformed from the present loose system of several million individual farms, efficient though they may be, into a tightly knit, fully coordinated organization of larger and larger units operating on the assembly-line principle. The trend in this direction is already evident; it has been increasingly pronounced, year by year, for the past decade. Marginal farms, barely capable of subsistence production, are being abandoned at a faster rate. Good small farms, even in some of our best agricultural areas and once providing a more than adequate living for a family, with a little money in the bank, are now being sold because investment and overhead are out of all proportion to the return. Good large farms still in the family class, manage to survive by virtue of intelligent management and hard work. Nevertheless, pressure on these efficient units is becoming hard to resist as corporation farming spreads. This relative innovation consists in the acquisition of a number of adjoining farms and operating them as a single unit. The so-called "corporation" is financed as any business corporation is—managers, foremen and hired help are furnished the latest machinery, and the system functions the same as any efficient factory or industry.

Such a "factory in the field" at present may cultivate up to several thousand acres. Given a suitable location of many small farms, there is no reason why they could not expand such holdings several times, with shareholders clipping coupons in distant city offices. The situation is precisely the same as that which confronts small business, the independent store or shop, for example, in competition with chain stores or big factories. A small profit per unit produced accumulates to substantial sums as the volume of production expands, an expansion the independent operator cannot achieve.

Now we come closer to home base, dairying. The dairy business is just as vulnerable to bigness as any form of crop farming, even more so because of the increasingly strict enforcement of sanitary regulations, which crop or livestock farmers do not have to contend with. Otherwise they face the same financial problems of investment and overhead which year by year bite deeper into profits. There are milk factories now which manage several hundred to a thousand milking cows. Every phase of the operation is streamlined. The cows never know the freedom of open pasture. Hay, silage and grain are provided by conveyor belts, manure is loaded by conveyor chains, sheets of rubber composition or cork replace bedding. At milking time cows are moved to the milking parlor, where one man attaches eight machines to eight cows at a time and the milk passes through glass pipes to bulk tanks. One man can milk about a hundred cows an hour. (By contrast, with two machines I milk ten cows in a half hour.) Sometimes replacements are purchased, sometimes they are raised, with close attention to blood lines to assure as far as possible high milk production, though there is never a guarantee that even the daughter of a champion milker will measure up to her dam. The average life of a cow in such an enterprise is five to six years, her prime years, for few cows can maintain the maximum output demanded over a longer period. The herd is well cared for in every way, but constant emphasis is on top production and cows are usually "burned out" after several years of unceasing pressure. Sanitary regulations are rigid and milk does not even come in contact with the open air. Here is the cow as a machine.

From this extreme, which is destined to become commonplace, the scale of individual dairying descends to my kind of operation, with the average in between running to about forty-cow operations, a steady increase in recent years and certain to continue upward henceforth. It is the only way a dairy farmer can maintain an adequate income. Year by year his investment grows, his overhead mounts and the price he receives for his milk trends downward. He knows there is a milk surplus, or that he is headed toward one, which depresses prices; but, as with crop farmers caught in the same squeeze, higher production is the only answer.

As a result, milk quotas are just around the corner of the milkhouse. There appears to be no other way to regulate milk supply and keep it within the bounds of consumer demand. Each farmer will be allotted a production figure, based on his pre-quota production, and for that controlled milk he will receive a fixed price. Any surplus will sell at a much lower rate and be used for cheese, dried milk and similar by-products. These quotas will be transferable to the new owner if a farmer sells his farm and herd. Such a system would benefit the farmer in that he would be assured of a reasonable and stable price, but it would also impose a limit on his operation. If his costs continue to mount, and there is scant ground for anticipating that they will remain at present levels, then he can expand only by buying another farm and herd to boost his production level. This, of course, is what the ambitious, efficient dairyman will do, either with capital he possesses or that he can borrow.

He has children, his wife rightly wants her share of worldly goods, he appreciates the importance of education in a civilization that demands college training and specialization, and he will do his utmost to guarantee such benefits. The small farmer, who insists on staying small, will disappear, either because of age and sons who have little if any inclination to take over his operation with its hard work and skimpy financial return, or because of sheer economic pressure before he gets old. For the really small operator, such as me, the knell already rings a little louder. Eventually I foresee not only a ceiling quota on milk production but a floor quota. That is, if a dairyman is not producing enough milk to rate as a viable economic operation, he will be excluded. Moreover, in the managed society that certainly lies just ahead, I agree that such restrictions will be justified. Harsh, beyond question, but incontrovertible, an inexorable extension of the change that has been taking place in farming and business in recent decades.

There is another aspect of dairying that will bring increasing pressure on the small dairy farmer and may oblige him to seek another livelihood, perhaps even faster than the quota system. That is ever stricter regulation of sanitation. This, very evidently, could be used to impose so many requirements on the small farmer as to render continued operation impossible. And again, there would be no recourse from rulings based on sanitation. They are beyond argument. You submit or you're through. The tendency in this direction has been evident in recent years.

Milk intended for the New York milkshed, such as mine, is

subject to inspection by the field man at the creamery that buys my milk and by an inspector representing the milkshed. Each has full privilege to appear at any time and examine every phase of milk production from the cow and her environment to the milk that is trucked to the creamery. There must be a clean barn and surroundings, clean cows, clean utensils, a clean milkhouse, even clean water in the cooler, where evening milk must be kept at a temperature just above freezing until the following morning. At the creamery, each farmer's milk is dumped separately and examined for sediment, then tested for bacteria count. A quick warning is returned if there is sediment; a quick visit by the inspector follows if the bacteria count reveals an increase. Unless there are flagrant violations and carelessness, the field man avoids being a martinet, simply because part of his job is to maintain a friendly relationship with the farmer. Not so the state inspector. His word is law; he knows his authority and is prepared to wield it with finality. Within limits he is likely to be reasonable, pointing out faults he has noted and according grace for a few days, after which, he announces, he will return. If faults have not been corrected by that time, he will ruthlessly ban your milk for several days to a week or until every objection has been remedied. To argue with him is not only futile, it is stupid, for he objects violently to being crossed and the angrier he gets the heavier the penalty he inflicts. I know of one instance where a single milk pail was not in its proper place on a rack in the milkhouse but standing outside exposed to dust. The inspector's reprimand angered the farmer and words were exchanged with increasing heat until the inspector walked away, having condemned all milk for seven days. That represents a serious financial loss, a severe fine for letting one's temper get out of control.

Some of the stipulations on the score sheet which the inspector checks as he strolls about, border on the absurd, dreamed up by an office man who probably has never been in a cow barn. For example, one recently added item reads "Covered milk pails." I was scored as not having covered milk pails, though I was unaware of this until after the inspector had left for I have found it prudent to study the sheet in private, curse in private, then wait for the next tour of duty to ask questions. On this matter of covered milk pails, I queried other farmers. They scoffed at the idea, repeatedly demonstrating that it is impossible to remove the cover of the milking machine and pour with the other hand and at the same time get rid of the pail cover. If the cover is taken off first, where can it be placed without gathering bits of straw or sawdust which later fall into the milk? I talked with a dealer in milking equipment. He had never heard of such a pail. So I had my defense well in hand when the inspector next appeared.

"Covered milk pails don't exist," I informed him.

"They will some day," he replied blandly. "They aren't official yet so I just check it against you without insisting that you get them. Later they will be a must."

I asked him how they would operate. He didn't know. That was still to be figured out.

Another new regulation is that there should be a light bulb for every three stanchions. But there is no mention made of wattage. In other words, four or five 25-watt bulbs would be according to the rules but would not provide as much light as two 100-watt bulbs. Some milking equipment is just as well hung up in the barn as in the milkhouse, thus saving an extra trip twice a day. The score sheet, however, demands that it be carried to the milkhouse.

The impracticality of such exactions irritates the farmer.

The inspector's attitude likewise riles a dairyman who, by and large, is more than willing to abide by the law. I have long felt that the inspector would establish a much better relationship if he occasionally, and of course when warranted, offered a word of praise, however faint, for evident cooperation. That, I fear, is too much to hope for. An inspector seemingly must restrict himself to adverse criticism. Commendation would be a dangerous aberration that would weaken his authority, place him on too friendly a basis. So he takes no chances, remains strictly within his sphere of dealing out rebukes and penalties. I often wonder whether he manages to unwind when he is home with wife and children. Or does he go on carping?

A recent innovation in dairying is the bulk milk tank, which appears certain to be added to the list of required equipment, representing an outlay of $3,000 or more, a sum which most small farmers simply cannot afford. The old system, still widely practiced, meant pouring milk from the machine into a pail, then into a milk can; or sometimes directly from in the machine into the milk can, which was transported to the creamery. The bulk tank is installed in the milkhouse and as a cow is milked in the barn, the milk is drawn through glass or plastic pipes to the tank, thus avoiding all exposure to air or to humans. It is quickly cooled in the tank and held until a large tank truck arrives and pumps the milk aboard. The system has obvious sanitary advantages; and it remains to be seen whether, or perhaps how soon, these will be judged of sufficient importance to make bulk tanks compulsory. If so, it would be a lethal blow to many small farmers, apart from the expense involved. Many dairy farms are located on dirt roads that frequently would be impassible in severe winter weather for the huge tank truck that collects milk. Even with the old system these farmers are frequently obliged to haul their milk by tractor to a hard road where the smaller truck that loads the cans is able to get through. Even in good weather the wear and tear on a tank truck would be severe. My hilltop—and it is not unique in location—can be impossible for traffic for days at a time, the four-wheel drive of the jeep making it the only vehicle that can then buck through the deep snow. Bulk tanks, therefore, would be out of the question for such farms.

The weeding out of small farms is already noticeable and the rate is sure to accelerate as the economic pinch increases, a pinch which will become hardship if bulk tanks become mandatory. As the present small farmer grows too old to handle his work, and his children depart for jobs of eight-hour days, five days a week, the farm will be crossed off the list and probably sold to someone working in a nearby city but preferring to commute. That is the modern pattern, and it is rapidly expanding.

Impetus to this trend may be provided by various plans being put forward to assure jobs for young people as they attain their majority. One of these proposes a change in the rural school curriculum. At present rural schools place considerable emphasis on vocational agricultural courses, which until recently seemed logical. But as farming becomes big business requiring big capital, with automation a major factor, small farming or employment on farms offers far less opportunity than industry. Therefore, it is argued, vocational skills other than agricultural should be emphasized in rural schools, not to the exclusion of the latter but to bring it into better balance with regard to future jobs. This makes sense since industry can and will expand, whereas farming assuredly will not expand, and probably will contract, as a job source.

I mull over these various aspects occasionally, parked under a tree and with nothing else on my mind for the moment. And I become increasingly convinced that I am one of the last individuals with the privilege of buying a small farm and making a modest go of it as a dairying enterprise. If, perchance, a reader of this book has that inclination, my urgent advice is to get started without delay. No more than five years hence, he may encounter so many obstacles, even actual barriers, that he will be unable to satisfy his longing for a rural livelihood. If I am right, this represents a definite and regrettable loss in the American way of life. Heretofore an individual has been free to choose his way of life. Dissatisfied with job or surroundings he could pick up family and belongings and move to the green pastures that are always on the other side of the fence. He might succeed, he might go broke. If so, he could try again beyond the next fence. This is no longer true. Not that he is forbidden to move, though in my more sour moments I foresee even that, but that he is no longer sure of finding work more to his liking. Skill is an essential these days, in any work; the opportunity to learn new skills is becoming more limited and skills are more intricate, demanding longer time to master them. These facts, linked with the growing need to stabilize work forces in those areas where jobs are available, cannot help operating against the fluidity of movement that has heretofore prevailed.

Before concluding this gloom-and-doom review of small-scale dairying, I should append a few figures as further evidence that the drift toward big-scale dairying is not likely to be arrested. Right now the dedicated young man who insists on dairying as a career almost certainly is, and had better be, a college graduate, with considerable prior experience and liking for dairy farming. Lacking these primary qualifications he is headed for disaster. If he is lucky enough to inherit a growing farm he naturally is off to a good start. Nevertheless, he must face the fact that, when he has a wife and children to support, his enterprise will represent an investment of close to $50,000—farm and buildings, herd, machinery. An operation on a smaller scale simply would not return the income sufficient to raise and educate his children and provide the amenities which both he and his wife desire and deserve. Granted such auspicious circumstances and all his labor, every day in the year managing some forty milking cows and fifteen head of young stock, he will do well to end the year with a net gain of $10,000, with $8,000 probably the more realistic as an average.

That is a sizable sum, though not riches, but he must also realize that it represents the peak that he can aspire to as a one-man business. No matter how hard he toils, he cannot get beyond that figure without expanding to more cows, more land and hired help. Then he will be nearing the border of big business.

As for the young man who does not inherit such a layout, who must start from scratch, the outlook is decidedly grim, regardless of how ardent a devotee of dairying he is. He can, of course, start on a more modest scale with the intention of enlarging year by year, but that will be a slow, frequently discouraging task. If he takes the big gamble, with financing from a bank, he will bind himself to a debt burden for just about the rest of his life. Surely some evening he and his wife will sit down with pencil and paper, do a bit of hard figuring and come to the conclusion that a forty-hour week in a factory, with all its drawbacks, would be preferable to such a struggle. And there would be one less dairyman.

The lucky youth in the first instance might also, in one of his less optimistic moments, do some figuring. His $50,000 inheritance, if wisely invested, would bring in about $2,000 annually without effort on his part. A forty-hour-a-week job would return a steady income, with week-end leisure, and the opportunity for advancement would promise better pay, even the possibility of promotion to the upper brackets. Devotion to dairy cows would be hard put to it to resist such temptation. And another farm would go up for sale.

6.

Enough of dark glasses. Let's change to the rosy-colored variety. We are on High Meadows. With the Arab we say, "What is, is. What happens, happens." Life is still good. Let others worry. A glance out any window is reassuring.

There is the garden to the north. A sudden thaw in February has wiped away more than a foot of snow and the lawn emerges so green and fresh that I think of the power mower and one more extension of grass, the final one I vow, to be chewed out in the spring—chewed out of thick, matted quack grass, causing the mower to shudder and groan, even expire if I don't yank it free in time. Yet, after a year of repeated cutting, quack grass can be convinced that it should abandon its coarse, rank ways (the cows scorn it, fresh cut or as hay, I have learned) and become lawn. Not perhaps the velvety emerald turf that England boasts but nevertheless acceptable unless too closely studied. Year by year nature's process of the jungle taking over has been reversed, and clipped green grass has pushed back the luxuriant growth of burdock, milkweed (so handsome in the fall, the dried pods like clinging birds while the fluff floats away on the breeze), ragweed (an infusion of it cures diarrhea), pigweed (the first young leaves good in salad), and thistles, where the goldfinches assemble to stuff themselves with seeds before resuming their lilting flight and gay piping.

The final patch of lawn will bring it even with a big soft maple, beneath which I have set a flagstone bench. Its lines, I claim, are early Doric for it could hardly be simpler—three narrow rectangles of stone sunk upright in the ground for support, one fine six-foot slab of trimmed flagstone, laid on top, held solid by its own weight. And to complete that corner, about seventy-five yards from the house, Scoop next summer will get a thorough physical workout by rebuilding the last twenty feet or so of stone wall, long since reduced to a straggling heap by successive frosts and thaws. He has rebuilt all the stone walls close to the house, taking overweening pride in the capping job, which means laying trimmed sheets of smooth stone along the top to obtain a straight, level line. He is a more meticulous worker than I, and the results add enormously to the appearance of the place, the house and terrace on a slight eminence, the lawn dropping away on three sides. Last fall I planted a number of forsythia branches and young multiflora roses in the several low spots next to the wall that are difficult to manage with the mower. And on the other side of the wall, scrub wild cherry sustains a huge canopy of grapevine and hops. From my Doric bench I study the splendid pattern in stone that is the fireplace chimney and recall the man who built it, another of those real artisans still found in the country.

Scoop and a school pal of his drove the stone-boat and the

horses when the fireplace and chimney were added to the new house. Old Sid was persuaded, with some difficulty, to lay the stones. Only when he decided he would enjoy the work would he agree to a job. Thus at one time he became a good trombone player with a small dance band. Later he became fascinated by the intricate skill of violin making, so he made violins. Fine cabinet work was no less than a passion with him for years, but at all times masonry was his special love. Not brick laying. He declared that bricks were monotonous, that even an expert job of bonding and pointing resulted in a flat, drab surface. Stones, particularly of our local variety which have been harvested from the fields by back-breaking labor and then laid to form the miles of stone wall still extant, these were ideal material for Sid's artistic taste. He built his own big house with them.

"Get me big chunky ones," was his continuous command as he and the chimney mounted slowly toward the ridgepole.

Lots of stones were rejected after one glance but soon the boys caught on to Sid's taste and were even gratified by his occasional praise.

"That's the kind, dammit," he would exclaim, tonguing with extra pleasure the ever present tobacco quid. And he would hold up admiringly a thick stone about a foot across, with at least one square corner and an uneven face covered with gray and bluish lichens. "Fetch me more of those."

And his platform moved up and up again. There was no monotony in the surface he produced with the tons of stones brought to him. Horizontal lines were broken before they became repetitious, vertical lines were curved for the most part, large surfaces were varied by small adjoining surfaces. He used a minimum of mortar, troweling his pointing deep between the stones to achieve a striking pattern of shadows. He paid close attention to color to obtain both variety and harmony. Yet all in all he worked fast, requiring only three days to finish the job, broad at the base, with two sloping shoulders and the straight column surmounted by the capstone. For this I went to the quarry (how often have we made use of that wealth of flagstone) and had a piece of carefully selected stone an inch thick cut to dimensions. Sid laid the four small corner posts, and the boys climbed to the roof to aid him as I hauled the slab up and it was set in place. There it still stands, keeping rain from entering the chimney and increasing the draft, defying hurricanes and furious winter winds. Not the smallest stone has budged in the entire edifice over ten years. Sid's monument is a major feature of the house.

To the unacquainted eye my garden is hard to make out during a winter thaw that has bared the grass. Several years ago I abandoned plowing and harrowing for the garden and since than have relied on a mulch of old hay to cover the patches I dedicate to vegetables and flowers. After thawing and freezing throughout the winter the mulch has disintegrated and is lost in the ground. I recognize the several patches but mainly for the purpose of fixing other spots for next season's horticultural efforts. Except for two perennial fixtures, the asparagus bed and the red raspberry patch. Even the strawberry patch is shifted every two years.

The asparagus bed has been the most rewarding part of the garden for time and labor invested. Year after year, toward the end of April, I begin to poke aside the heavy mulch along the two lines where the crowns are set, searching eagerly for the first white tips that will announce that the season has started. Thereafter for two full months asparagus is a daily dish, twenty to thirty handsome spears to each cutting. And how we love it. It is the one vegetable with which I have no desire to exercise my bent for concocting new dishes. I want my asparagus newly cut; boiled gently in salted water to the exact point of tenderness, somewhat comparable to that of spaghetti known as *al dente*, the delicate state hovering between crispness and mushiness; then served on a hot plate and buttered generously, with a little salt added. What a treat for the taste buds. Table manners are relegated to second place. As with lobster, clams on the shell, and spaghetti, I am purely pleasure bent. I subscribe wholeheartedly to the French and Italian attitude. Niceties should never hamper gustatory enjoyment. You can't possibly savor all the delectableness of a lobster without intimate encounter, accompanied by loud sucking sounds, snorts of ecstasy and a certain amount of dribbling. Clams are so much more flavorsome when sucked from the shell and the shell drained of juice. If a bone retains a morsel of meat I crave at that moment, why shouldn't I pick it up and be appeased? Think of the psychological torment I induce by not so indulging. Away, then, with exaggerated etiquette that forbids one from displaying hunger, even flaunting it. There is nothing revolting about hunger or the satisfying of it. I am not entirely averse to the complimentary belch of the Chinese. So up with a succulent spear of asparagus, properly bathed in butter, pop it into the mouth, munch on it rapturously (including the butt end if it is cooked as it should be), then wipe the chin openly and without apology.

As for other vegetables I have come to be guided by value received for work expended. For instance fresh peas, young, tender, sweet, can be had at their best only when grown in the garden, picked at the right moment, and cooked without much delay. Bought in stores they are by comparison almost another vegetable, and a poor one. Yet two sowings, ten days apart, are all that are worth the effort in these parts because hot dry weather sets in come late June and peas that mature then have little flavor or sweetness. On the other hand, such vegetables as green peppers, egg plant, and broccoli are just as good if not better than mine when bought in a store. I am not one of the green-thumb addicts who boast about the great variety of produce in their gardens as proof of their toil and talents. I prefer spare time to read a book.

Green beans I plant in successive quantities and they are decidedly worth the effort. Beets, for baby buttered beets and in salads, also for beet tops, among the best of the greens, are better from the garden. Likewise, young zucchini, the lowly radish, young carrots, young cabbage—and, of course, lettuce and romaine. Sweet corn, true Golden Bantam, I have been obliged to give up growing, with deepest regret. The raccoons reap the harvest far ahead of me. Traps are no defense; poisoned bait might be eaten by the cats, which might also get caught in a trap; even a fence of chicken wire will not foil coons with their keen appetite for corn. They climb right over it. I am outraged and greatly distressed in spirit when I go to a corn plot and find the coons have been there, pulling down ears that need another week or more to ripen, stripping back the husks just enough to permit gnawing off a couple of rows, then moving to the next stalk, and on and on, in sheer and wanton destruction until I am lucky if I wind up with a few nubbins. It is too heartbreaking to warrant another try. Woodchucks I have been able to control by placing traps just within the entrances to their burrow. They can be as much a pest as coons, especially in lettuce, peas and beans. However, I note recently that, as I extend the lawn, eliminating brambles and weeds along the stone walls, they are less of a problem for they prefer not to expose themselves over considerable distances.

100

However, I am not deprived of fresh, picking-to-pot corn, praise be, for we all love it—on the ear, cut off and gently fried in butter, in soufflé or pudding, and especially in old-fashioned succotash, which means diced bacon boiled with the corn and lima beans. That rates high on my seasonal culinary calendar. Store corn, of course, has been picked for hours, even days, and has lost its crisp sweetness. Fortunately I know a nearby farmer who grows sweet corn commercially. I can go there anytime and gather a couple of dozen ears, leave the money in a specified place if he is away, hurry back home and pop them into a kettle of boiling water. A very close rival to my own garden corn.

With corn, as with some other garden produce, I do object to the hybrids. The hybrid sweet corns mature earlier, bringing higher prices to the grower, and the ears are regular and attractive, but they lack the proper sugar content. Real Golden Bantam corn is still without peer. My farmer friend's goal is to get as much corn as possible to market as early as possible, and he therefore plants the early hybrids. I eat them but not with the avidity that comes later when his plots of Golden Bantam reach their prime. Then I become gourmand and gourmet, devouring butter-drenched ears to such a state of repletion that I can survive the long months ahead until the next season with equanimity.

Late in July the first green tomato displays a faint flush of pink. Then there is excitement in the garden. Every morning the transformation is more noticeable and I become impatient for the day when I can pluck a glossy red globe, firm yet yielding to an exploratory thumb, and regale myself with one more of the garden's finest rewards. How easy to understand that once the tomato was avoided as poisonous! The bright red is so showy, the fruit (berry?) stands out so prominently that it gives the impression of an overexaggerated effort by nature to trick the innocent. It would have been more appropriate than the apple as a symbol of evil for wayward Eve. And the Spaniards who found it in South America called it "love apple." Instead, nature was at her generous best and I render thanks. From early August till the first frost, even afterward if I have had advance warning and cover the remaining fruit, tomatoes appear daily on our table. Vine-ripened, picked at peak flavor, they are vastly superior to the greenhouse variety or those picked half-green and ripened on the window sill.

An ideal summer lunch is a bowl of tomatoes, baby beets, and string beans, nested in lots of crisp lettuce, all coated with a dressing of fine olive oil, wine vinegar, a little mustard, garlic, chopped parsley and chives, and salt and pepper. Bread, butter and a piece of cheese are all that need be added. Later in the season I make several quarts of spaghetti sauce with garlic, onions, mushrooms, sweet basil, and tomatoes, all simmered with olive oil until reduced to a thick paste. I also make tomato jam, whose full fresh flavor is a welcome surprise on a cold winter morning. But for the most part our tomatoes are eaten raw, in the garden with the dew still on them and a palmful of salt, or at table, day after day, desire never waning.

If I am lucky, freshly picked mushrooms (*Agaricus campestris*) go into that spaghetti sauce. On a cool morning after rain in August or September, I have occasionally gathered a basketful in an hour or so. They are most unpredictable, abruptly disappearing from one portion of pasture, popping up in another. The search itself is a pleasant walk. They are hard to overlook; the white caps gleam against green grass or brown earth and are visible at a surprising distance. Cultured mushrooms are very acceptable but growing wild gives them a special tang. I grill them in a hot iron skillet, with butter and salt added after they brown and begin to wilt. They are a valued addition to almost any dish—stews or sauces, with meats or fish or crab.

The asparagus bed gets a heavy dosage of manure every year and the soil is extra rich. There I frequently find mushrooms of giant size, six to eight inches across. One of them grilled is equal to a beefsteak.

Finally I must mention leeks. What has happened to the estimable leek? There was a time when a packet of soup greens was a grocery-store staple and leeks were always included. Today they are impossible to find in a store, and a request for them brings forth a bundle of green onions! Urban friends report that they are absurdly expensive in New York if they can be found. Yet they are a delectable vegetable—"poor man's asparagus," the French call them, and with reason. Boiled leeks with butter or a slightly sharp French dressing are a wonderful first course for any meal. Boiled and covered with a cheesy white sauce and browned under the broiler, they provide a vegetable dish that rhymes neatly with steaks or roasts. Yet I have not found a single farmer who grows leeks, so easy to raise and resistant to early frost. When dug up with roots and dirt they keep for weeks in the cellar, providing one of the requisites for a pot of vegetable soup, the flavorsome broth of which can be the basis for a variety of other soups. Instead farmhouse trash heaps are dotted with empty soup cans, a really lamentable comment on modern country living. It is not only the economic factor that is involved; it is the superior quality and taste that one savors in home-made soups.

I don't expect to meet with *cordon bleu* cooking in the country, different sauces, herbs, long-tested combinations of meats and vegetables that require care in preparation but can no longer be improved upon. Farm fare as a rule is simple, a meat-and-potatoes affair with gravy intended primarily to fill the belly and topped off with sweet cakes or pies—a heap-up plate to sustain a working man plus the sweets he always craves. Those of foreign origin, after one or two generations have abandoned special native dishes, Polish, Russian, Lithuanian, German and Italian, all of them delicious but demanding painstaking preparation. I have talked with various of these oldsters and they all give the same reason—the young people refuse to spend so much time in the kitchen. Frozen foods, whole frozen dinners, even frozen pastries, are preferable, for they are ready to serve in a few minutes with no bother. Even Italians are surrendering to frozen pizzas, frozen ravioli! *Dio mio!*

The country kitchen now revolves around the home freezer, not the stove. That capacious innovation contains all the elements for a meal. Three or four packets are selected, thawed out and cooked. What could be simpler? Some of the packages may have been working their way toward the bottom for many months but—they are edible. They still provide nourishment. Taste? The cook shrugs an uninterested shoulder. I am quite aghast when a farmer friend tells me that one of his heifers cannot be bred and that he has turned it over to a butcher. The butcher, for payment in cash or in kind, carves up the animal into steaks, roasts, chunks, and grinds mountains of the less choice cuts, a total of about 500 pounds of meat. Into the freezer it all goes. Obviously, some of those packages will not return to daylight for months, possibly a year. To begin with it is not prime beef—a young cow is not intended for prime beef; to end with, it is rather indescribable. I am not entirely opposed to frozen foods, to be sure. During the winter I buy frozen vegetables and find them acceptable, though at best they fall several grades below the garden-fresh product. Frozen fish is only a fair substitute for fresh. But I do object to frozen meat. It loses flavor and texture in the freezing-thawing process, and after months in its benumbed state it merits the fate that Ben Jonson accorded a salad—"Throw it out the window." A decade or so of such diet at least should condition us for the transition to repasts of algae. A steak, thick, deep red, nicely marbled, is an object to be revered. While such are available I will show my respect in the eating, trusting the algae era will be after my time.

Economy is not a sufficient reason for overwhelming one's self with hundreds of pounds of meat. There are real economies to be found any day in a good meat market, but I have discovered they go begging. Veal kidneys, for instance, were disdained by the customers in this area and thrown away until I learned of it. Now, whenever the butcher buys a side of veal, I get the kidney—two if it's a whole carcass—and the menu hits a new high. Broiled in the fireplace or slowly cooked in a casserole with a bit of onion, a pinch of thyme, a handful of mushrooms, a little dry mustard and a dollop of port wine— either way they are regal food. I have offered to pay for them, to be certain one might be claimed for cat food, but the butcher refuses. They would be thrown away otherwise. . . .

Flank steaks are virtually unknown hereabouts. Yet flank steak, scored, then broiled or fried, holds its place with the best sirloin. Though coarser in texture, it nevertheless possesses a distinct flavor much to my liking. But the butcher is obliged to put it into ground beef. So for an excellent variety of steak I pay the same price as for ground beef. Brisket, cheapest of all cuts, meets the same destiny until I am in a mood for boiled beef, with carrots, a few leeks and some greens, or decide to corn some beef in a big crock. One way or the other, hot or cold, it rates high praise. Except from other customers. Why? I wish I knew. Perhaps it is mere habit, years of familiarity with a few cuts of meat and no curiosity to experiment with others. Anyway, such a lack of the adventurous spirit is to be deplored.

Still another example. The butcher cuts up chickens for sale according to customer preference. This leaves necks and backs which he packs in cellophane bags, several pounds to a bag, and then offers to his trade. Yet even at the absurd price of a quarter for a bagful he meets with few bidders. When they are tossed into a pot with an onion, carrot, bay leaf, maybe some celery tops, and simmered for a couple of hours, I have a couple of quarts of delicious chicken broth, fine as it is for soup, perfect for adding to other dishes. Moreover, if one wishes to pick over the bones, enough meat is gleaned for a fine *pilaff* and the remains make food for the cats that they tie into with rumbles of delight. Yet how few people will bother.

We are lucky to have an excellent small meat market only a few miles away. Top-grade meats are the inflexible rule, and over the years my relationship with the proprietor has risen from new customer to customer who wants and knows good meat to friend who gets anything he asks for, who is privileged to go behind the counter to pass judgment on a porterhouse steak ready to be severed from a quarter of beef—even, if I happen to arrive a bit after noonday, to being invited to lunch in the tiny backroom. Lunch consists of choice of the shop—beef steak, veal steak, pork steak, lamb cutlets, grilled to individual taste, with bread and butter. No frills here, and not much leg room beneath the small table. But the butcher is a true meat eater of the old school and I am more than willing to rival his gusto as we attack our oversize steaks and discuss changes in popular taste in recent years, for example, the almost unanimous rejection of fat, due seemingly to illusory economic reasons and also to American dietary obsessions. The economic reasons are not valid because the butcher buys a carcass, fat and lean, for prime beef must have its proportion of fat, and when he retails it he must charge for the fat whether the customer takes it or not. Thus, round steak, trimmed of all fat, will cost slightly higher per pound than the same steak with its fatty periphery. I know another butcher, in a smaller general store in a village, who declares that he cannot sell prime meats because of the larger percentage of fat, since his farmer customers will not pay the price he must ask for the fat-denuded cuts of meat he tries to sell.

My only qualification as commentator on the pros and cons of diet is my own experience and my observations during my residence in Europe. For myself, I insist on a modicum of fat with any meat because it complements the taste of the lean. At the age of sixty-seven I fail to notice any deleterious effect on my physical well-being. Butter, moreover, is a generous component of all my cooking. This, however, does not warrant generalization. That "One man's meat is another man's poison" may well be true. Physical make-up is in endless variety. On the other hand, Europeans have no horror of meat fats, quite the contrary, and I know of no statistics indicating that heart disease there is caused by or increased by animal fats. In addition, in France and other countries, except Italy, *cuisine au beurre*, cooking with butter, is deemed essential to a superior menu, without any evidence of impaired health. Again, in Holland, Denmark and Norway, where butter consumption is the highest in the world, the prevalence of heart disease is the lowest.

So with boldness that may backfire on me, I asseverate that

high blood pressure is far more common here than abroad because of the fast pace of living and the inability and the lack of opportunity to relax, with resultant tensions. Living in Europe, one enjoys a broken rhythm—a more leisurely start in the morning, a two-hour interlude at midday, an occasional pause if the afternoon is long and strenuous. Tensions have scant opportunity to build up when intensive work alternates with relaxation and, I like to add, only a glass of wine or a mild apéritif to enhance relaxation instead of two or three high-powered drinks gulped down American-style at the close of a long day of sustained effort. Is it logical to assert that the saturated or animal fats probably do accumulate as cholesterol in the arteries but that the accumulation becomes a danger only when blood pressure rises beyond the danger point? Would not the menace of heart disease be minimized if blood pressure were controlled by a saner mode of living? Could be. It's my opinion and I stick with it. Which affords me the pleasure of eating whatever I like without a qualm. And of relaxing.

I used to read cookbooks as zestfully as I read good novels or, say, such histories as De Voto's vivid account of the fur trade and the mountain men in *Beyond the Wide Missouri*, Mattingly's splendid *The Armada* and others. Not any more. Having stored away the basic principles of French cooking and having various cookbooks available for reference when a complicated recipe is desired, I now indulge in culinary inventions, concoctions that tend occasionally to get out of control but that usually are thoroughly edible with the additional tang of being more or less my own, if only because of one or two alterations, sometimes improvements, in a book recipe.

To start with there is always wine in the cellar, white and

red. Some twenty years in Europe accustomed me to wine with meals and I have made no effort to alter the habit. Wine, I maintain, is good for a person, good for health, for digestion and for one's outlook on life. A glass of wine before dinner perks up the palate, gives a final whet to the appetite and abets relaxation during the pause it necessitates before sitting at table. The day's work is done, the pace slackens and comes to a halt. And a little wine combines with repose to permeate one with a gentle lassitude that dismisses the day's worries and mishaps. In that mood, food becomes more exciting and the entire digestive process is brought to its finest functioning. Laughter refuses to be barred from such a sense of well-being. And when good cheer prevails, body and mind are in harmony, life is wonderful.

Wine is also an important, sometimes essential, part of cooking. It can make all the difference between a drab, untempting dish and one with exciting aroma and memorable flavor. This is increasingly recognized in the United States and I applaud every evidence of it that will bring more unbelievers into the fold. Farm periodicals, as a rule so staid and conservative in all approaches, fearful of offending their pious readers, indicate occasionally, all too rarely thus far, a loosening of editorial rigidity by mentioning wine as an adjunct to good cooking. All too frequently, however, their daring is mitigated, even annulled, by ignorance of wine values. I was appalled by one recipe for a beef stew that recommended rather timidly at the end that some people might find that wine would add to the stew's tastiness, "any wine, red or white." Pity the venturesome soul who takes the recommendation literally and, chancing to have some sweet white wine handy, dumps a glass of it in with the beef. Almost certainly he or she will never repeat the experiment with a dry red wine and so come to glory.

After all, the recipe was followed, the stew was ruined and the unhappy episode is best forgotten—except for counsel passed on to friends to the effect that wine has no place in the kitchen; the decisive "I know, I tried it" condemnation. And wine in cookery suffers a severe setback.

For the uninitiated I repeat the general rule that red wines go with meats; white wines with fish, seafood and chicken. Later the novice will learn that mackerel can be baked in red wine, as in Brittany; that white wine is a boon companion with veal in certain dishes. I combine them in a kind of stew that is basically French, though with my own variations. Breast of veal is so cheap in my vicinity that it is virtually given away. But what delectable fare it can make. Cut it in serving pieces; cover them with two-thirds water and one-third dry white wine, and add an onion stuck with two cloves, two carrots, chopped parsley, bay leaf, a pinch of thyme, two cloves of garlic, whole peppers and salt. Simmer three-quarters of an hour, remove the meat, sear the pieces lightly in hot butter in a skillet without browning them, and sprinkle a little flour on them as they are stirred. At the same time strain the liquid and reduce it by about half by fast boiling. Add this to the meat and simmer another half-hour or until very tender. Remove from fire, stir in two egg yolks very slowly, add a little cream and a little lemon juice. Keep hot without allowing to boil until served. It is a dish requiring napkins and a bold flaunting of table etiquette; for the bones must be picked up and sucked for full savoring, and the sauce must be mopped up with crusty bread, amid peeps of deep satisfaction.

Here is a simpler dish that will delight any palate, discriminating or not. Place pieces of chicken, legs and halved breasts, in a shallow buttered casserole; brush with butter and put in a very hot oven for five minutes. Turn the pieces, brush with butter and return for another five minutes. Mix half a bar of melted butter with a cup of dry white wine; add a spoonful of minced onion, chopped parsley, salt and pepper. Pour over, cover and return to oven for about thirty minutes; then uncover and bake another fifteen minutes until chicken is tender and brown. This is excellent served hot in summer, but it is even more enticing on a hot day when served cold with a plain lettuce salad—and, naturally, a bottle of chilled white wine, though a bottle of cool rosé wine is equally acceptable.

Fresh fish are hard to come by in these parts. Ardent fishermen are not lacking and the state does an excellent job of stocking streams with trout and bass, but only twice has my friendship with anglers been signalized by my becoming the recipient of a recently expired trout. Two notable events. Since I have lost all urge to spend a day wading our local streams, much as I like fish, I must make do with frozen fish; and, as I've said, though I am prejudiced against frozen meats I find frozen fish a fair substitute for the newly caught. Steaks of haddock, halibut, swordfish and salmon are usually available and add variety to the weekly menus. I am especially pleased when I encounter frozen smelts after the spring catch, for they are among my favorite varieties and do retain their special flavor. Baked in white wine with sliced mushrooms, cut chives and a little butter, they deserve to be placed in the feast category. However, wine is not at all essential in cooking fish, and frequently a simple frying in butter or deep fat is the more appreciated.

Fortunately, oysters in bulk, so fresh that I defy anyone to distinguish them from those in the shell, are to be had throughout the winter and they are invariably on my weekly list. However, as I have yet to discover an improvement on either raw oysters or a rich oyster stew, I stick with those two methods. Clams in the shell can always be obtained during the summer by ordering in advance. They also are eaten raw for the most part, and Scoop and I can polish off several dozen at a time with undiminished zeal. They appear in stews and once in a while in chowder, but I find chowder more appropriate in winter. Not often do we have them in such quantity that we steam them, though I have a great liking for them when steamed in dry white wine and butter. As soon as the clams open and their juice mingles with the wine and butter, remove them, pour the sauce into a bowl, sprinkle it thickly with chopped parsley, and then gather round for a treat to the taste buds. Take a clam in the fingers, break off one shell, suck the clam from the other with a loud whistling noise, then dip up a mouthful of sauce with the shell. Marvelous in hot weather.

Frozen oysters, canned oysters, canned clams have long been stricken from my list, but canned crabmeat deserves more acclaim than it gets, at least in these parts. Since it is easy to prepare and distinctive in flavor. I am surprised that I am almost the only buyer of it in our local small-scale supermarket. White wine can be used in cooking crab, but I prefer sherry for a little extra zest, with cool white wine as the accompanying potable. Try the following on a summer day: Pick over crabmeat to remove the filaments. Make a rich sauce of butter, flour and cream and, when it is thick, stir in two egg yolks, with some lemon juice, a tablespoon of dry or cocktail sherry, paprika and chopped parsley, and the crabmeat. Pour into a buttered shallow casserole, top with buttered bread crumbs and bake until the crumbs are brown. You will get politely urgent requests for second helpings. If it is too hot for cooked food, mix crabmeat with a small amount of mayonnaise, some sharp prepared mustard, green peas if available (raw if they are young and tender), raw grated carrot, raw diced celery, chopped parsley and chives. Serve on crisp lettuce, or, if you wish to be elegant and tomatoes are in the garden, scoop out the tomatoes and pack the shell with the crab mixture. You will be regaled.

Imported sherries and ports are indubitably superior to our domestic varieties, but the best California sherries offer close competition and New York State ports are not to be spurned, and both are decidedly cheaper than the imported. The best French table wines are without rival, but the best California table wines are every bit as good as the second-best French wines and also are less expensive. Therefore, since wine is used in small quantities in cooking, seldom more than a glassful, it can add hardly more than a few pennies to the cost of a dish, and those few pennies are amply returned in flavor. If a glass of cold sherry were to replace the ubiquitous cocktail or slug of whiskey as a pre-prandial potion and a little wine were drunk occasionally with meals instead of sweet, fizzy soft drinks, the general health graph might well turn a bit upward.

Port wine likewise has its place in the kitchen as well as being a congenial potion with nut meats, when guests are too pleased with life to move from table and it is quite enough to lean back and talk. I use port with those veal kidneys I get free. The kidney is split lengthwise and trimmed of the cords and most of its fat. It is then seared in a generous amount of hot butter in a casserole. A tablespoonful of minced onion, sliced mushrooms, chopped parsley, a good spoonful of prepared mustard and a third of a cup of port are mixed and poured over the kidneys. The casserole is then covered, and the dish baked in a moderate oven for forty-five minutes, being basted occasionally. Port also makes a new dish of that old standby, baked apples. Fill the cored apples with sugar, dot with butter, sprinkle a little cinnamon on them, bake with a cup of water for fifteen minutes, then add a cup of port, and baste every few minutes until done.

As I said earlier, red wines are the usual accompaniment in cooking meats, but this is not invariable. Since in the spring a good cook's fancy turns to lamb, so here's a lamb stew that will bring rave notices from your friends. Cut shoulder lamb into pieces. Chop a few spring onions and cook lightly in butter in a large casserole, add meat and brown it, dusting it with some flour and stirring well, also salt and pepper. Cover with beef consomme and a cup of white wine; add a bay leaf, a pinch of thyme, chopped parsley, a sliced carrot or two, and a pinch of marjoram. Simmer for about an hour or until very tender, adding a cupful of fresh green peas for the last five minutes. Boil pared potatoes separately and serve with the stew. Hot biscuits also make good blotters for that gravy.

As for cooking beef in wine, there is so little chance of going wrong that recipes are superfluous. Just try a glass of red wine in your next pot roast or beef stew. It will make a welcome change. On the other hand, wine is wasted on, even detrimental to, beef that is fried or roasted, including ground beef. Finally, pork simply does not adapt itself to cooking with wine, perhaps because it is fatter than other meats. The only exception I know of is a slice of smoked ham, seared in a little butter, than fried slowly with a dash of sherry. That is excellent.

A few words about eggs—first to lay the menacing ghost that is widely accepted as hovering about to ruin omelets, reducing them to flat, heavy masses; that scorches them; that may even flip the omelet onto the floor. A light, moist omelet is the easiest thing to produce in the kitchen, and most of the usual ritual can be thrown out the door. Don't use more than six eggs to an omelet, which is ample for three people. If there are more guests, make another omelet. Break the eggs into a bowl and beat them gently with a fork, just enough to mingle the whites and the yolks. Add salt and pepper. Heat an iron skillet piping hot. Put in it about one-third of a bar of butter and spread it around so that it melts fast and begins to foam. Turn down the fire to very low. Pour in the eggs. As they thicken around the edges, fork them toward the middle, without stirring. Where there are pockets of uncooked eggs, open the bottom and fork aside cooked parts to enlarge the hole. When the entire surface is still moist, take a spatula and turn half the omelet on top of the other half. Place on a hot plate and serve at once. It should *not* be brown on the bottom, just golden. So doing, you will offer a delicate, light omelet of perfect texture and taste. All in about ten minutes, from eggshell to table, where guests must be waiting, fork in hand.

Slow cooking, advisable for any meat, even broiled steak, is especially important with eggs. An egg is a delicate object to begin with, and quick, high heat changes its consistency to a rubbery quality that is objectionable. When poaching an egg, drop it from a cup into swirling boiling water and immediately reduce the flame to very low. An extra minute will be required to attain its finest point of soft yolk and barely firm white, but the delay is well worth while. Low heat likewise makes a vast difference in fried eggs, scrambled eggs, even hard cooked eggs.

Omelets and scrambled eggs can be varied almost endlessly. With omelets it is usually best to spread the lightly browned mushrooms, the heated tomatoes or what else you wish on top of the omelet just before it is turned and served. An *omelette aux fines herbes*, with chopped parsley and chives, should be

115

combined before it is poured into the skillet; the same is true of a cheese omelet. A good omelet makes a surprisingly hearty dish, winter or summer, though I find it particularly tempting on a warm day with a tomato and lettuce salad to top it off.

Good appetite! It comes to everyone and is satisfied in almost as many different manners. As a biological necessity it can be quelled in a hurry by guzzling a quantity of meat, vegetables and pie, washed down with cold water or hot coffee, until repletion signals that the eater will survive till the next meal. This is remindful of De Voto's description of his mountain men who, as they moved indomitably into the primeval Rockies in search of beaver, found buffalo were scarcer so that when one was killed a Gargantuan appetite demanded a Gargantuan gorging. The liver of the huge beast was eaten raw as a special morsel. The choicest cut was the ribs carved from the hump, denoting a quantity of fat along with lean meat. These were spitted beside the fire and only partly roasted before the odor was too much for the ravenous trappers and they seized the ribs and started to demolish all but the bones, though if they contained marrow they were cracked and sucked clean with equal greediness. The fat was highly prized and the men's faces, beards, coat fronts and hands were soon glazed with congealing drippings. On they went, undeterred and far from satiety. While there was meat on the carcass they glutted. Every man was good for eight to ten pounds of meat, until the stomach was crammed. And after a nap, many returned in a couple of hours for another several pounds of roasted meat and fat. Even the intestines, pressed clean of fecal matter, were gulped down raw, a yard or more at a time. Repulsive? Not at all, considering the circumstances. Such hunger, mounting during days of subsistence on berries, roots, even boiled rawhide, merely reveals how narrow is the gap between man and animal, a gap that has been widening for ages but is still hardly more than a hairline.

Those mountain men were far from civilization, in fact hardly civilized, preferring a life akin to that of the savage Indians they constantly encountered. A hundred and twenty-five years later, their frontiers have vanished and we are the heirs, with civilization crowding us from every side. Yet we still get hungry, at times almost as famished, we feel, as they were. And we can satisfy such hunger with an endless list of tempting edibles from all parts of the globe. By raising eating above sheer necessity, making full and imaginative use of the abundance we have, perhaps we widen that gap by another fraction of a thread. Good food, good wine, good company combine to whet the mind as well as the palate; conversation flows more freely, new, even original ideas are forthcoming, gaiety is an inspiring sauce, and when the table is quitted, the spirit has been nourished more than the body.

That we have made sure of at High Meadows, whether there are the three of us or a dozen. We enjoy the surroundings that are conducive to good appetite and leisurely dining. Open meadows, woods which in some spots seem still haunted by bear and an occasional Delaware, are an invitation to a walk that will revive hunger. There is work of one kind or another that can be shared with volunteers who feel the need to stretch disused muscles. The air is clean and bracing; on a dry, cold winter day it becomes so heady it is like inhaling pure oxygen. And there is the flagstone terrace with one part shaded by the grape arbor, a fine old cherry tree beneath which a table can be placed, or the fireplace in the living room after an hour or so in the snow. There is mulled wine or buttered rum for those desiring a quick glow of warmth while the fire is leaping beyond the shin-heating stage. And eventually—who is in a hurry?—the fragrance of good food will be ushered from the kitchen to the dining table and we will fall to. Ah yes. Good appetite!

7.

"You can't beat this, can you? Let's never go back to the city. Just stay here, with blue sky, clean air, no racket. Where can you do better?"

Thus the week-end guests on an August afternoon. Wearing a minimum of clothes, they stretch out in chairs on the terrace, soaking up sunshine for that mandatory summer tan, thrilled when driblets of sweat attest to the sun's heat. Or they park under a tree with a book for somnolent reading or wander in the woods, kicking up generations of dead leaves as sharp contrast to the unyielding sidewalks they tread most of every year.

During the winter, notably at Christmas, another kind of weather prevails but the reaction is the same. "What air! And the snow. How white and clean." Rather than drive over snowy roads they come by bus to a nearby town, where I pick them up in the jeep. We roll through superb country scenery —sloping fields of radiant white, gray stone walls capped with a thick frosting, pines and hemlocks bowing beneath their white burdens, even a pond where young skaters rush about, slide, fall, scream their delight.

"We'll gather greens for the house. Have a drink before the fireplace. What a holiday!"

Arrived at the house they throw snowballs, trip each other, wallow in the snow. They laugh noisily, chatter wildly, are supremely happy.

Do I join in? Most certainly. Any time of the year when friends are overjoyed by what the farm offers, I can match their enthusiasms, just as easily now as during the first days when I found magical perfection in its every aspect. Nevertheless, I am increasingly aware that I have two attitudes, two minds, am schizophrenic if you wish, but in a rather benign form. Experience has led to a realistic outlook that accompanies my more natural romanticism, not obtrusively but ever present and occasionally commanding my attention.

On a hot summer day I laugh and talk with my rollicking guests, but now and then my eye will stray to a nearby meadow and note that pasture is getting increasingly brown, that the trees are losing their luster. I remark the cows, sharp against the horizon of East Meadow, how they are on the move more than they were a month ago, as dry weather checks the growth of grass. And I think of the spring, whose flow slackens when rain is lacking. In winter, while holiday celebrants welcome the keen air and the deep snow, I take a moment to scan that clear blue sky they have been admiring and wonder how low the temperature will fall by morning if a cloud cover does not intervene, or if the light wind blowing gains in power and causes drifts about the barn doors. Before a long array of concomitant problems take hold, I return to the fun; yet I know that before I go to sleep I shall consider all the possible difficulties that may be present by daybreak.

For weather is dominant throughout the year in my rural existence. It is everything from implacable foe to outrageous whimsy to benign partner. It can bring exuberant joy today and unbelievable woe tomorrow. And as has been so often said, there's little that can be done about it.

I have read Virgil's *Georgics*, followed such counsel as, "If indeed thou wilt regard the hastening sun and the moon's ordered sequences, never will an hour of the morrow deceive thee, nor wilt thou be taken in the wiles of a cloudless night." What entrancing prose but, alas, follow his portents as closely as I can, I have been ingloriously deceived, again and again. I have studied almanacs, pored over meteorological charts. Sometimes they hold true; then, just as my faith has started to rise from repeated disappointment, down it goes as cataclysm descends from the sky when I had counted on a lovely day. I am an addict to weather reports, received by radio. If people are about, I command complete silence at certain intervals during the day when the forecasts are scheduled so that I can hear every word, ponder subtle hints, weigh the eventual effect on my hilltop of weather conditions observed in the Midwest and the Southwest, on the northern plains, even on the Pacific Coast.

I plot low-pressure cells and high-pressure cells until I am fit to be put in a pressurized cell, check wind directions and velocities, but seldom do I come up with the right answer. Nor do the boys manipulating the high-speed calculators. I have investigated the jet stream and my one conviction there is that in winter it has swerved too far south, which lets in untold masses of frigid air and snow out of Canada. Since Canada is a friendly neighbor, why can't we arrange a treaty whereby she keeps all those arctic air masses well north of the frontier?

I have been known to break off milking, late for some reason, just to run to the house, flip on the radio and listen to a prediction. It has become a mania, more than mild. And it continues though I am long since convinced that I face defeat, that the most professional prognostications will not be fulfilled. The only exception is when the forecasts are of the worst character. They are most likely to hold up, and they, of course, are the ones I don't like to believe, actually seek to prove wrong. Therein, I fear, is my weakness. I accept predictions that fit my desires—rain if it is dry, clear if it has been rainy, warm if it is cold, cool if it is unbearably hot. I seek to refute those contrary to my wants. My losing column is always the longest. I went through a session of disciplining my preferences into the exact contrary of my scheme above. Still I lose. The law of averages simply was not made to include the weather. I can't win.

In no way am I criticizing the men of the weather bureau. I imply no negligence on their part. They do their utmost, with great dedication to their task of trying to predict the unpredictable, of analyzing sheaves of reports from far-flung stations to reach a seemingly flawless conclusion only to have a quirk of temperature or pressure upset the entire pattern in a matter of minutes. They deserve unceasing sympathy. What could be more frustrating, more wounding to pride, than to be a daily open target for merciless public criticism because their elaborately contrived forecast went sadly awry? A tough spot to be in. However, progress is being made toward greater accuracy, in tracking hurricanes, for instance, but I fear it will not be in my time that a weather prediction can be accepted with full faith and dependability.

I met my first hurricane a few years after World War I when two friends and I sailed a thirty-six-foot yawl out of New Haven, Connecticut, and headed blithely for the West Indies. On just one score regarding that venture can I speak with certainty: we learned a vast deal more about deep-water sailing during that trip than we knew at the start. Anyway, we eventually reached Beaufort, North Carolina, laid in various supplies and put out again for points south. We ran into rain and a high wind, furled the jib and jigger, figuring we could run due south not too far off shore. Then the wind hit with full fury, the mainsail was taut as a board and full out against the stays, and all we could do was run with the wind, away from shore. We had a bad night. Time and again great bearded combers overhauled us from the stern and cracked down on the vessel, actually burying it so that whoever was at the wheel had to stand at full height to keep head above water. And each time the yawl shuddered and rose above the surface, shedding cascades of water, getting ready for the next assault. Toward morning we noticed that water in the cabin was rising more than could be accounted for from what leaked through the hatchway. All too obviously, the terrific pounding the boat had suffered had opened a leak.

Now the situation was definitely grim. We were at least fifty miles off shore, the dinghy had a hole stove in the bow, there was no hope of starting the soaked motor to work the main pump, and the hand pump was quite inadequate. We were wet through despite oilskins, chilled to the bone, plain miserable, yet, curiously enough, not frightened. (We agreed later that foundering seemed so inescapable that we were beyond panic.) There wasn't anything to talk about, nothing to do, except to try to warm up with a slug of corn whiskey we had bought at Beaufort. I finally decided, as cook, that I might try to make coffee over alcohol in the galley. I waded up to my knees through sloshing water in the cabin, sympathizing with our bedraggled kitten who had taken to a small hammock over one bunk; and as I was drawing water at the sink I spotted a crescent of light at the base of the sink's drain pipe, where it passed through the hull. A finger pressed close to it detected a slight flow of water from the outside.

I let out a yell that brought Tommy from the cockpit, Steve staying at the wheel. There was no question that the leak was located and the whole grim picture changed at once. We at least had something we could battle. While the boat was pounding, we could not stop the leak from the inside and there was nothing we could do outside. After some debate we agreed that the only solution was to bash the pipe clear, then hammer a plug into the hole. Tom went for a slightly tapered wooden capstan bar in the cockpit. We compared its end with that luminous crescent as well as we could through heaving water and decided it would fit, a close fit, we admitted, but worth a try since we had nothing else to work with.

That was a genuine *momento de verdad*, moment of truth. With the pipe broken away, a hole more than an inch in diameter would be wide open. If the bar was too big too enter, we were all too literally sunk. So we got set, Tommy with the bar close to the outlet, I with a heavy hammer. I socked the pipe, widened the crescent, socked it again and the pipe was clear. Tommy shoved the end of the bar into the hole and, by golly, it entered as much as an inch, snug as the tightest champagne cork. I tapped the top end to drive the bar in as far as it would go, and then not a trace of that gleaming new moon was visible. I made coffee which we laced generously with white mule and drank in grinning toasts to each other.

The hurricane blew itself out an hour or so later. As we

steered for shore, distant by a totally unknown number of miles, the sun came out, and we spread clothing and bedding on deck to dry.

Late that afternoon we sighted land, and a powered fishing craft, putting out from a narrow inlet, came alongside and took us in tow to navigate the twisting channel—and there we were, cozily anchored in a sheltered bay identified as St. Lucie's Inlet. As we approached the channel our pilot pointed out three sailboats, two larger than ours, careened high on the beach beyond tide mark, victims of the storm. We had been lucky. So we went ashore that night in wet, filthy clothes, for which we were smilingly pardoned by the hotel keeper, dined and drank sumptuously and slept in big, dry beds while our clothes went to the hotel laundry, to be ready in the morning.

Such was my first and only hurricane up to my taking over High Meadows. At the time I vehemently affirmed that it was quite enough to suffice a lifetime. The weather has not concurred. Several full-fledged hurricanes have visited the hilltop during my sojourn, along with fledglings and a variety of gales. None of them has threatened me with drowning as the first one did, but they have come too close to inflicting disaster for my aging comfort. I can get along very nicely without them. The one menaced removal of what was beneath; the others seek to tear loose all that is overhead.

The inaugural hurricane walloped the hilltop in November, 1951. Like all its successors it came from the east, blasting over the ridge of East Meadow and descending by an unimpeded path straight for the house and barn. Apparently, like all downhill movement, it accelerated by some Einsteinian formula of original momentum times the square of the distance multiplied by degree of slope. At least that approximates the effect when it hit the house. By official anemometer recording the wind attained ninety miles an hour. That, however, did not include my local formula. With it came walls of rain—deluges that slammed against the house with the impact of a solid, not a liquid. The rain, perforce, traveled at the same speed as the wind and was absolutely horizontal when I observed it between house and barn. Layers of water were clearly discernible, some denser than others.

The new house leaned with the repeated bursts of violence, shivered and creaked through all its new timber. The rain was blasted inexorably between windows and frames normally almost airtight. Mary and I did what we could with rags and cloths to keep ahead of the flood, dashing from one to another of the east windows, but it was a losing game. Water seeped through the upstairs floors and dripped mournfully into the living room and kitchen. Then the power lines went down, not unexpectedly but nevertheless adding measurably to our feeling of utter helplessness. Hoping to find a little cheer by gazing out the west windows at all the rain that had passed the house and was pouring along to some other target, I found no comfort in seeing an occasional shingle ripped loose from the roof and riding the wind like a kite. That meant more leaks to cope with. I gave up in disgust, stretched out on a couch and read a book on astronomy, trusting that if I could lose myself in cosmic space where whole giant galaxies were rushing away at several million miles a minute, our hurricane would be reduced to a puny disturbance unworthy of notice. The idea may have been sound but it was not entirely successful.

At midafternoon I went to the barn. Bella was in the maternity ward and I wanted to check to see if all was progressing well. Twice during that brief walk I was obliged to

126

drop to my hands and knees just to remain stationary. As I opened the barn door I was blown right through the aperture and found myself in almost complete calm. I could hear the wind and rain but dimly and there were my incredible cows, showing not a hint of perturbation, chewing stolidly, glancing toward me as I entered, then back to their hay when they recognized me. It was a wonderfully soothing moment. All the turmoil without was as far away as those galaxies I had been tracing. Moreover, Bella had calved and was lowing proudly as she polished her wobbly infant with such exuberant licks of the tongue that the calf was toppled repeatedly onto the bedding. I complimented Bella, scratched her ears and informed her that the calf was hereby dubbed Windy, which certainly was appropriate.

The wind and rain abated later in the afternoon, and I managed the milking on schedule. Without electric power there was, of course, no water in the drinking cups and the vacuum pump for the milking machine was not operating. However, there had been minor power failures before and I had had a petcock set in the manifold of the car. I ran the car into the barn and connected the petcock to another one in the vacuum line by means of a length of rubber hose, and thus obtained sufficient suction by letting the car run at a little faster pace than idling. So I avoided milking by hand, a task at which I shall never be proficient. Before dark I was able to turn the cows out to drink at the trough by the springhouse, and I was back for dinner just a bit behind schedule.

The power was not restored for thirty-six hours. There was ample irony in our predicament. Though water was still visible throughout the house we didn't have a drop for drinking or cooking or washing. So I hauled water in a bucket from the old well beside the house.

Let me say right here that power service has been vastly improved over the past decade. We are served by a Rural Electrification cooperative and it does an exceptionally good job. Power failures now are rare; and when they do occur as a result of severe storms, repairs are made in a hurry so that electric light is almost never lacking for more than an hour or two. Only government backing could have extended power into such remote areas as mine, with the countless advantages it brings to farmers.

I have lost track of the full or near hurricanes that have pounded the hilltop since the initial one. Even the names of the worst ones are forgotten. Not that I have reached the point of being indifferent to them. Yet over the years memory of them becomes blurred; they are so mingled with other events, pleasant and unpleasant, that they lose separate identity. Nevertheless they leave a variety of woes in their wake, necessitating extra work: roofs to be repaired, for instance, especially when the barn loses strips of roofing paper and rain wets the hay. They come but they go and after a bothersome interval, life regains its serenity. What does stick indelibly in the mind is the impression of awesome power possessed by these aspects of nature running amok. Generally it is latent, tucked away in some cranial recess so neatly as to seem forever lost. Then comes a radio announcement of a possible hurricane forming far to the south in the West Indies. If it gathers force, it is tracked closely, and then sometimes the word comes that it is plainly headed in our direction. That is when the recess opens, memories revive, and all the potential dangers come to front and center stage to demand recognition. That interval of waiting just before the storm breaks can be much more harrowing than the storm itself.

Two instances of such unleased violence might be mentioned. In 1955, deluging rain accompanied a hurricane. Every creek and brook in the region became a wild torrent, pouring into the larger streams and transforming them into rivers boiling far over their usual banks. The power of the surging water was irresistible. Soil was gnawed from around roots and great trees fell like sticks, concrete bridges collapsed, large areas were inundated so swiftly that humans and livestock were gulped down. After the storm had passed the whole countryside was filled with the reverberating thunder of rushing water. It was of such tremendous scale that there was no room for terror.

The other occurred in 1959 when a sudden and penetrating thaw in January sent the Susquehanna River on a rampage. During its wild course a weak spot developed in its bed and a huge hole was torn open leading into a coal mine shaft. For hours a big share of the river poured into the shaft and then on to connecting shafts until it finally filled entire mines. I can never get that picture out of my mind—almost a whole river abruptly going underground. Estimates were that some forty billion gallons of water churned into the mines.

Those two exhibitions of nature on a binge brought floods to the hilltop, of course, but no irreparable damage. The barn had to be bailed out; otherwise we were well above the havoc in the valleys.

A surfeit of water or a dire lack. That is the usual, the accepted pattern now at High Meadows. Only one summer since our arrival has been to my liking regarding rainfall. That was 1960, and I was the only farmer hereabouts who enjoyed it. With no crops or hay to worry about, with lush pasture my one overweening desire, I welcomed cool, wet weather in April, May, June, even into July, by which time the pastures were still in such good condition that the cows had fine browsing until September was far advanced. Everybody complained but me. In fact, I was compelled to restrain my expressions of pleasure because they brought forth such sour looks from my neighbors, such profane resentment, that friendship could easily have curdled. So I restricted my exulting to hilltop privacy, where I gave it free rein.

All my other estival experiences have been radically different. Year in, year out, there has been rain in May and June, when haying is at its peak, little if any in July and none in August except for a rare thunderstorm. Pasture dries up, grass turns brown and I go to the springhouse every other day to check the water flow, which diminishes when rain is lacking.

The springhouse contains a concrete vat holding about a hundred gallons. The overflow passes into the drinking trough, then into West Meadow. What I must watch closely is the amount of water running into the vat. When it gets low, the cows can drink the vat dry at evening milking unless the supply is replenished by the spring. Naturally, the cows are thirstiest in dry weather, finding little if any moisture in the grass they eat, and when they reach the barn they battle for first go at the drinking cups, one to every two stanchions. And they must have water to maintain milk production, as much as twenty gallons a day.

Now, as I've said, there is an old well beside the house, a good thirty feet deep. In other days it supplied the household with water, the cows getting their ration at the spring. Later the pipe was laid from the spring to the house so that a pump and pressure tank could provide water for the house. Then a pipe was laid from house to barn for water for the cows, and the well was abandoned. My contribution to this plumbing arrangement was to hook the well onto the pressure tank so that I could turn on either the spring or the well for water.

However, the well gets low during a drought and must be used sparingly as a supplement to the spring. If this system is understood, it will be apparent that I must engage in considerable footwork.

About halfway through evening milking, I make a fast trip to the spring. If the vat is down to only one more action by the pump, which starts and stops by a pressure valve, I must dash to the cellar, shut off the pipe from the spring, turn on the one from the well. Thereafter I am reduced to prayer that the cows have already had their fill, that I shall not have to watch them apply their muzzles to the cups and gulp water for minutes on end, while I gulp for air.

As a rule the system works, the cows are satisfied and I can turn them out with the expectation of a full quota of milk in the morning when, happily, they will be less thirsty. Nevertheless, I have had to haul milk cans full of water from the farm below, an additional chore I loathe. A filled milk can weighs some 120 pounds and is awkward to handle. It must be held in readiness in the springhouse and dumped into the vat when the latter is about to go dry. I have timed the whole procedure: five minutes to fill a can or thirty minutes for the six cans the jeep will hold, time for the trip down and back and for unloading, and a good hour has passed. If as much as three loads are required per day, when the spring and well are practically non-existent, all my leisure has vanished and I am in a bad mood.

At the beginning of our annual dry spell, Mary gets in even more of a dither than I do. Every morning she asks about the water supply. I try to reassure her, with the now accepted stipulation that we must not use water in the house just before I start milking, so that the vat will be full, both morning and evening. During the day, some laxity is permitted, as well as after evening milking once the vat begins to fill again. About noon water can be drawn for cooking purposes, drinking water is stored in the refrigerator and Mary informs me she has had a shower.

"Hardly a pail of water," she vows. If I tell her that she is privileged to take three pailfuls she feels outraged. Her plan is set awry, her sacrifice is not appreciated. I grin then and agree that a pailful was sufficient.

Guests arriving in August are subjected to a kind of indoctrination. Mary explains the very serious water situation in great detail, leaving visitors somewhat baffled by the intricacies of the problem but firmly convinced that for their own welfare and a continuation of friendship they would be wise to abjure water entirely throughout their stay. Which does not disturb the wine bibbers who, after all, comprise most of the invited.

I still laugh at one bit of comedy owed to our perennial drought. One hot afternoon when the spring was reduced to a pencil-size trickle, Mary and I were in the house, the coolest place we could find. Mary answered a knock at the door. There stood five girls and five boys, some carrying knapsacks, all dusty, hot and tired. They explained that they were hiking to a camp, still some miles away. They were very thirsty and all had an urgent desire to use the toilet, an urgency so insistent that the girls had no compunction about making it known. I remained in the living room where I could hear the ensuing conversation without becoming involved myself in an obviously explosive situation.

Mary explained about our water shortage, politely but firmly, concluding with the strict command that the toilet was *not* to be flushed after each one made use of it. The girls were ushered in first—two at a time because the bathroom is small. Hardly had the first pair closed the door than we heard the all too audible rush of water.

Mary banged on the door. "Don't flush that toilet. I told you not to."

Timid murmurs from within.

The girls were roundly scolded when they emerged and the next pair was admitted only after being shrilly cautioned as to the flushing process. After a brief, tense silence, *swoooosh* went the water. Mary shrieked, stomped her foot, seemed on the verge of tearing her hair in proper fictional style. Again utter silence. I was tempted to call out that the hour was early enough in the afternoon to permit wasting a few gallons of water, but I have learned that there are moments when my interference does not contribute to a restoration of tranquillity. I swallowed laughter and waited. And by golly if the *swoooosh* was not repeated.

Mary yanked open the door, yelping her rage, her defeat, her loss of faith in humanity. I could picture the two abject, apologetic faces of the guilty as one of them said meekly, "You do it without thinking. It's mechanical."

Which did not allay Mary's near hysteria. She escorted the fifth girl through the door, announcing that she intended to stand there to thwart by physical intervention any move resulting from sheer habit. As for the boys, they were shooed off back of the barn, not worthy of being trusted. At last they all took to the road, giggling as they departed. It was some time before Mary cooled off and it was weeks before I could convince her that there was a comic element in the whole episode.

I am not given to prayer but there have been many occasions when I have felt a strong urge to emulate the medicine men of another age and offer sacrifice and incantation that might bring rain. Sitting on the terrace, I feel, at the first sign of a dark cloud in the west, that some form of persuasion might be developed to cause it to expand, grow blacker and more ominous, become so pregnant with rain that the long-needed downpour would descend on the hilltop. Frequently the patch of cloud does spread over the western sky, but there appears to be a formation of terrain, a series of higher ridges or broader valleys just beyond my horizon, that channels thunderstorms to the north so that they by-pass our immediate area. The cloud thickens, its white periphery exaggerates the deep purple at its center and the mass begins to move toward me. Lightning flickers, thunder booms far away, soon I feel the cool, damp breeze that betokens a storm and I am more hopeful, sure that rather strenuous body English is steering the storm directly to me. Then the auspicious breeze dies, the big cloud swings along the horizon and the rain that I can often see falling favors fields miles away from mine.

Thunderstorms are exciting spectacles. When one does manage to leap that distant barrier and take an unswerving course toward the house I am fascinated. The huge cloud boils inwardly, black masses curl upon each other, rifts open with a bright gleam and swiftly close, angry shreds of vapor wrench free only to be sucked back into the dark maw. Lightning becomes more purposeful, thunder causes the earth to tremble and now, when the precursory wind strikes it is clammy, with definite power. And over the farthest ridge a gray curtain of rain appears, marching steadily over tall trees and through intervening valleys. That is the part I find most thrilling. Onward comes that wall of water, the wind begins to whistle in the eaves, a chair blows over, leaves swirl up and down in the clashing currents of air. Rain has conquered the last ridge, it swoops down into the last valley, and the first big drops smack onto the terrace. I stand up, ready to run for the door but eager to be a participant up to the very last moment. A bolt of lightning rifles down into my woods, and the boom that follows is deafening. Sometimes I can hear the struck tree crash. Then the welcome deluge is upon me. I reach the door, see the cows high-tailing across the meadow toward sheltering trees and watch with intense pleasure as rivulets form in the road, pools gather and overflow, the soil drinks and drinks.

8.

THAT WOULD PROBABLY BE IN LATE SUMMER, with autumn soon to make itself felt with cooler air and a sun that is losing its intensity. As winter approaches, a new set of problems must be coped with. During my early years winters alternated with fair regularity between closed and open, severe and normal to slightly mild. Recently they have all been on the severe side, with lots of snow, weeks of bitter cold, and hardly a hint of the customary January thaw. That is when I must be fore-handed, anticipating nature's freakishness whenever possible to avoid real trouble and hours of extra labor.

I have indicated how, on three sides of the barn, the land slopes toward it so that all water from as far away as my east and south boundaries eventually joins in a turbulent race to my two barn doors, front and back. Over the years the daily passage of the jeep and various kinds of heavy machinery has deepened these two channels. One solution for this unwanted flow would be deep ditches that would guide the water away from the doors. But these would be unsightly and awkward to cross with vehicles. My solution is temporary in that it functions only during the winter, then disappears, which to my mind is the better way.

With the first frost, I lay a dike of manure several feet from each door, several inches thick. Once this freezes I am fairly secure, though from time to time I am obliged to increase its height because snow and ice accumulate against it, eager to flow over it in the event of a thaw. Snow, of course, will have to be shoveled repeatedly from before the barn doors, particularly the front one, where the northwest winds whip snow around the milkhouse and into two- and three-foot drifts against the door itself. By late February my passageway is banked on each side up to four and five feet. That means work, work that tests my vocabulary of profanity, when it must be repeated for morning after morning of bad weather, even twice daily if the wind persists. The work cannot be shirked. Not only must the roll-back door be kept openable, but also the snow must be prevented from packing in the tracks to such a height that the jeep scrapes its top against the lintel, an eight-inch-square oak beam. It is so low that the horses had to duck their heads in passing while I squatted in the wagon, a trick at which Molly was adept. Doc, not so smart as the elderly mare, frequently forgot it and banged his head with a thud that threatened to crack his skull. I knocked one jeep top right off its supports and sprung the windshield on one occasion. Usually I could come out through the door with only a rasping complaint from the top cross-rod against the lintel. This time, however, I wanted to back the jeep into the barn; and since I had learned that I could emerge without great damage, I failed to figure that the front wheels would now be high on the packed snow when the windshield reached the lintel. I was looking backward to steer when the grinding jar occurred, and before I could stop I was enveloped in the collapsing canvas top. I finished out that winter without my coveted cab for protection and the windshield down, exposure I far from relished when bucking a frigid, snow-laden gale.

There was also the preliminary job of cleaning the channel in which the door moved when it was rolled back. All the dirt and stones that had accumulated during the summer had to be dug out down to bed rock. Snow was bound to blow into the channel and likewise had to be cleared to keep the door free, a mean task in the pitch dark of a bitter morning. Far worse, however, was the ice that formed during the night after a slight thaw had melted the snow and water had run into the channel. That called for the crowbar, kept handy by the door, to pry the door loose from the ice that gripped it like concrete. Many a pail of near-boiling water I have drawn at the milkhouse and poured along the door bottom as a last resort. That scheme poses a hazard also because if the water is not swept promptly out of the channel, it freezes. That requires crowbar and pickaxe to chip the ice clear. My gloved hands become numb from handling that unbelievably frigid bar, but I must get into the barn to milk those cows.

For one spell of an entire month the ice got so bad night after night that I left the door open in disgust and despair. Snow blew in, a foot deep on the workbench and back to the inner door where the cows are stabled. That spectacle was so disheartening that I finally spent an entire day getting the door free. A door on rollers conspires in another way to compound my woes. When snow gathers beneath one end it rides up and the roller jumps the track. That invariably occurs on the most arctic mornings when I tend to hurry to get into the barn with the warmth-exuding bovines. So I regret my haste and, cursing, drag the door back until the roller can be slipped onto the track, a neat bit of juggling as I am obliged to lift the heavy door with one hand while fumbling with the other in the dark until the roller is in precise position so that I can give a shove and feel it hook onto the track. One way or another, harried and profane, I do get into the barn, finding some comfort in the fact that the cows are quite unconcerned over my tardiness.

If the wind has been blowing all night, which is quite likely, my first concern is the drinking cups. Are they frozen? Cows finish their hay about nine o'clock at night, then drink their fill of water, and, from then till morning hay, seldom touch the cups. Standing idle, the water at the bottom of the cups may turn to ice and the metal paddle that opens the valve cannot function. That requires a trip along the feed alley with a pail of hot water to melt the ice. That usually succeeds though there have been those unpleasant moments when water did not flow once the paddle could be moved. That meant that ice had formed in the pipe itself, and that a blow torch was the one answer. If I was lucky and applied heat at the strategic spot, all was well. If not, I had to play a game of elimination that might take an hour. My first winter the pipes froze solid, one section even burst, and the cows had to find their water at the springhouse until I undertook a massive plumbing job, something my varied talents had never been called upon to undertake. I dismantled all the pipe, section by section, took those plugged with ice to the cellar and stuck them in the furnace until they thawed, then screwed them back in place. Later I had thick insulating board put on the west wall of the barn, with every seam caulked, especially around the windows; and what with more cows in the barn, I have since been fairly free of ice in the cups.

Heating cable, a most helpful invention, keeps the water pipe in the milkhouse from freezing; and I have considered using it in the barn, but it would require nearly two hundred feet of cable, expensive both as an investment and in operation. The thirty-foot length in the milkhouse boosts the power bill about four dollars a month so the whole installation would add at least thirty dollars a month for constant use. That is not a huge sum, yet on a small dairy farm it represents an important item. So I put off the experiment, gambling on bovine heat to prevent serious freezing.

Heating cables, however, would not solve the major winter problem, and I don't believe anything in the realm of gadgetry could do so. That is the slow concentration of ice at each end of the barn. Some years this glacierlike movement begins with the legendary January thaw; other years, in late February. It continues throughout March. A day of sunshine with temperature above freezing starts the creeping assault. Water and slush inch along until evening, piling up against my manure dikes. There it freezes overnight. Several days of this results in a thick sheet of ice in front of the barrier. I add more manure, but if it does not freeze solid, water finds tiny channels, oozes through and meanders almost imperceptibly toward the milkhouse and barn door.

My first spring, before I knew enough to build dikes, I suddenly found ice at the milkhouse door and creeping inside. There was no way whatever to stem that viscous tide. Manure on top of ice is useless, for the flow passes beneath it. Frequently I have noticed a solid sheet of ice seemingly acting as a magnifying glass for sunlight and causing ice to melt below the surface and bubble along quite merrily as free-flowing water. Anyway, the upshot was that the milkhouse was invaded day after day, the mass froze night after night, and by the time warm weather arrived I was walking on a floor of ice a foot thick. That absurd predicament has not been repeated, praise be, but the threat returns every year, and is thwarted only by daily precautionary measures.

The jeep traverses these ice ponds with chains on all four wheels, which remain on throughout the winter for spreading manure in snow-covered fields. Cows, however, cannot be equipped with chains, and the smooth ice before the back door is dangerous for them when they are turned out for their daily stretch. For years I carefully spread ashes or cinders, the latter purloined from the township stockpile, and wailed loudly because I was obliged to repeat the spreading almost every day as new ice buried them. Finally I hit upon the idea of spreading old hay on the ice, wetting it down with a garden watering can, then urging it contemptuously to freeze. Which it did, thereby anchoring the hay and providing a carpet with such firm footing that the cows resumed their usual shoving and butting games. Moreover, at least a week of thawing and freezing was needed to cover the hay, whereupon another layer was forked out. Reduced labor and no risk of a broken leg.

Now, the water pipe from barn to house runs in a straight line, under the barn door and under the roadway and lawn, under the terrace and so into the cellar and the pressure tank. As I have said, the roadway has been worn down by a constant traffic since the pipe was laid some twenty-five years ago —certainly several inches, perhaps as much as a foot. Instead of being three feet underground, the accepted level to be below frostline, it is now not much more than two feet below the surface. The past three winters have been severe, with long periods of temperatures of zero and below. And three times, once each winter, the pipe has frozen, a serious situation that makes me a bit panicky. The thought of cows without water fills me with horrid imaginings of suffering and disaster.

The first time, I summoned the local garage owner, who has a truck on which is mounted a generator for the express purpose of thawing water pipes. He does a profitable business during every cold snap. He just did manage to get through the snow on my hill road and quickly ended the crisis. He hooked a cable end onto the pipe in the cellar, another on the pipe in the barn, started the generator, and heated the pipe until the ice melted. He then advised me to run a garden hose from the spigot in the barn to the outdoors and keep a trickle of water flowing to prevent freezing. That was simple and practical, I conceded, and obediently did as I was told.

But it is not quite that simple. A trickle of water is not sufficient on bitter nights. Ice forms about the end of the hose and gradually, inexorably, closes in until the opening is sealed. A flow of water at least as large as a pencil is essential to defeat the cold. This also presents a hazard. Unless the hose end is a couple of feet off the ground a stalagmite of ice rises bit by bit until it reaches the hose and engulfs it. Finally the section of hose lying on the snow and ice must be insulated from such contact by a layer of hay or feed bags. These precautions I learned the hard way. However, I had warning of freezing, for whatever reason, by way of the automatic pump in the cellar. As long as water flowed at a fixed rate, the pump had to start at regular intervals. If it did not, then it was up to me to hustle to the barn and inspect the hose, certain in advance that it had frozen. Possessed, luckily, of two fifty-foot lengths of hose, I would then unhook the frozen one, lay it out on the barn floor to thaw, attach the other one, and hope for the best. Because of worry over the precarious arrangement, it was not difficult to waken several times during the night and lie in bed listening for the pump. If it started, back for another nap. If not, into clothes and boots, out into the cold, and change hoses. I still cringe at the faint crackling sound of breaking ice when a frozen rubber hose is bent.

The second occurrence was more serious. One morning there was no water in the milkhouse. In itself, this did not upset me greatly for I could carry a pail of water from the barn as needed. Nevertheless, there was the likelihood that ice in the branch pipe to the milkhouse would spread and reach the main pipe. Once again the hoses were brought into action and I returned to my pump vigil. A few days later I noticed that the pump was starting more frequently and working for a longer period each time. This puzzled me until it dawned on me that the frozen milkhouse pipe had burst, causing a leak. For a brief moment I was cheered by the idea that this would obviate the use of hoses to maintain a flow of water. And it did work that way for another few days.

Until the rhythm of the pump began to quicken. Whenever I was in the house, I timed the recurring starts. The interval in between slowly diminished from a normal, considering the leak, of twenty minutes to eighteen, to seventeen and on down the disheartening scale. As water flowed through the leak, more of the ice melted, thereby enlarging the vent. All I could hope for was that the outflow would reach a maximum, then hold steady. If it steadied at a pump ratio of ten minutes, the situation was not desperate. No such luck. Day by day the count went down. Believe me, there was no tranquillity during those evenings when I would try to read and so forget my problems, only to have the pump start buzzing at seven-minute intervals, six, five, four and the very critical three. The pump could not stand much of that constant flicking on with ever-lengthening periods of pumping to get ahead of the leak.

It got hot, the smell of hot oil pervaded the cellar, the turbine began to grind alarmingly.

I tried the only remedy I could think of—digging a hole that would give me access to that damnable pipe. I trust I will never again have to undertake such discouraging toil. The only effective weapon was the crowbar against ground frozen solid, infinitely harder than ice, so hard that the crowbar bounced back from it as though it were iron. After ten minutes of lifting the heavy bar and banging it down with all my strength, I was able to scrape out a small handful of dirt and ice. If I gained two inches of depth in an hour I was making fast progress. With more than two feet to go! It was back-breaking, shoulder-shattering. Only my hands and feet were beyond sensation, because of the cold. I compared myself to Sisyphus but with no rewarding satisfaction. While I labored I tried to evolve an easier way out of my trouble.

One was to hire a couple of men to man the crowbar. Nobody, however, was interested in the cold, arduous labor I offered even at better than top hourly pay. The country attitude is that such problems are strictly personal and up to the farmer to handle. Then I came up with the idea of turning off the pump except when the cows wanted water, morning and evening. I hesitated over that for a time because it meant that the pressure tank would be drunk dry or emptied by the leak, so that the pump would have to be primed every time I turned it on, not a prodigious task but rather tedious. Also if water stood in the pipe it was more subject to freezing. Thus my mental squirrel cage continued around and around, eventually tossing out a new possibility.

What if I cut off the water to the pipe to the barn, by turning a knob in the cellar, then attached one end of my 125 feet of garden hose to the outdoor spigot at the house, ran the hose into the barn and attached the other end to the spigot there? Thus I would completely bypass the pipe itself, which would give the pump a rest; yet when I wanted water for the cows I could obtain it via the hose. I was elated, congratulated myself for being so bright.

Thus I got entangled in the most incredible kind of Rube Goldberg scheme that one might imagine. The spigot at the house had to be cut off and drained when not in use to prevent freezing; the three sections of hose had to be uncoupled, drained and hauled to the barn or the cellar when not in use for the same reason, then reassembled when needed, stretched from barn to house over snow and ice with a relentless wind blowing most of the time, screwed to the spigot and water turned on. Alas, I learned how difficult it is to drain every drop of water from a hose before ice forms in zero weather, no matter how fast I worked lugging hose into the barn about nine o'clock at night; and I learned that the concrete barn floor where I laid the hose was not conducive to thawing, and how swiftly a frozen hose can spring leaks. So I stowed the hose, all 125 feet, in the cellar, draping it about in serpentines and arabesques to assure drainage. Even so, it was not enough. If the cows failed to drink consistently and thus keep water moving in the hose, it froze. If it was bent in that stiffened condition, the rubber creaked and rasped and pinpoint holes opened. The night I turned on the water and headed for the barn only to note a number of tiny geysers spouting gaily from the hose, I admitted that I was licked. I rushed about with a roll of electrician's tape, working with bare hands in icy water to seal the holes. I was not too successful at that, but at least my labor sufficed to force some water to the barn. The next morning I drove to town, conferred with a plumber friend of mine and made my plight appear so desperate that he agreed to come up at once.

I returned, resumed my hacking at the hole in the ground with my crowbar. When the plumber arrived with a heavier crowbar and his father-in-law, the three of us took turns until by late afternoon we reached the main pipe where the branch to the milkhouse was connected. My plumber pal, bless him, managed to use a hacksaw in the narrow bottom of the hole, cut off the branch pipe, remove the end still in the main pipe and screw in a plug. Loud in my praise, I ran to the house and turned on the water. We all went to the barn for that triumphant moment of opening the spigot. But not a drop emerged. As I had feared, the pipe had frozen. That, however, was not insoluble, a mere trifle at this stage of the whole miserable ordeal. The garage man was alerted, he came up in the dark and put his generator to work, and at last there was water in the barn, the pump functioning normally while a length of hose kept the water moving, day and night. Thus ended my frigid session in hell, for that year. Peace was restored and I could devote my evenings to reading.

9.

With such an amplitude of experience to draw on, I forestalled water problems during the winter of 1959-60, though it was well below average for rugged weather. For the past few years the weather bureau seems to have established a record of its own for announcing new records in meteorological pranks—unprecedented maximums of snow or rain, minimums of rain or temperature, as though the elements were conspiring to make life more difficult, particularly for farmers. Some blame these excessive vagaries on atomic bombs but I know of no reason for agreeing with them. I am more of a fatalist—what happens, happens; what will be, will be. Whatever the explanation, March of 1960 was a fine example of weather at its worst.

I confess to a sense of weariness toward the close of every February. It is not of a physical nature, for I can still recuperate almost overnight from a stretch of hard labor. Rather, it is a fatigue of the nerves which gains imperceptibly in the winter months because of the host of uncertainties that must be faced, frequently for many days in succession. I know I magnify them unduly in advance. They are seldom as horrendous as I foresee them, and in anticipation I strive to reduce them to more realistic proportions. Then some near tragedy does descend upon me and I tumble back into the old rut.

On stormy mornings while I have my pre-milking glass of tea, I flip on the yard light to study the depth of snow, where the drifts are around the barn. Will the jeep be able to buck the snow and take the milk down? Shall I be able to get back? When the snow is deep I have to break tracks going down, and on the return climb expert steering is essential in order to remain in those two furrows; otherwise the jeep may stall or slide into the ditch on one side. On a few occasions I have chucked the milk into the cooler and waited until daylight when the prospect could be studied more thoroughly. But it is a challenge I dislike to shirk, and only extremely bad conditions force me to bow to caution. It is not so much the cash value of the milk that might be lost as the sense of defeat that I object to. Throughout the years I have yet to be completely stalled, but the margin of success has often been barely discernible.

More important is the problem of the manure spreader. When not in use, it is parked under the ramp to the haymows, which shelter it from snow and sleet. There I back up, hitch the spreader to the jeep and swing around to the back door of the barn. There, however, it is exposed to cold and the conveyor chains and bars freeze solid to the box. To have it thawed out and ready for use later in the morning, I haul it into the barn immediately after morning milking and leave it there with the cows until I am ready for action about nine-thirty or ten o'clock. Nevertheless, to get it there may require shoveling through a drift before I can even get the jeep to it, and this before dawn begins to show. Later I will scan the three meadows nearest the barn to decide in which direction I have the best chance of hauling the loaded spreader and then of moving when it is in gear, which adds a lot of drag for the jeep to cope with. My best hope, of course, is level ground, such as the field by the house. But a slope and a sharp turn getting there may defeat me. I can go down the slope to West Meadow, spreading manure as I move, but it is a long climb back when the spreader is empty. The garden back of the house is my surest bet and before a winter is over it usually is blanketed with layers of manure.

For spreading manure every day is vital to the smooth accomplishment of other barn chores. An accumulation of even two days becomes a burden that must be avoided at all cost. The sight of cows befouled from switching dirty tails is most depressing. Hence every stratagem is turned to to insure completing the job with the spreader. When they fail I have only the wheelbarrow for cleaning the barn. An unwelcome chore it is, for I can only shove it a few yards from the barn door and stack the manure there. Three years ago snow was so deep and drifted that for nearly a month the spreader was immobilized, and I watched the stack of manure near the barn grow to mountainous height while I forlornly contemplated the work accumulating for me in the spring when the entire mass would have to be shoveled onto the spreader and carted about. In the spring when the milk inspector pays me his semiannual call, the first place he examines is behind the barn. Manure piles are no longer permissible close to the barn, and I am curtly informed that I have seven days of grace. If the ground is not denuded of the last shred by that time, my milk will be suspended. The fact that he is entirely within his rights does not ease that hurried job of loading and spreading, loading and spreading.

As I say, these uncertainties and harassments begin to wear on me as January is crossed off the calendar; then brief February draws to a close. I think of March as a surly month, determined to keep winter alive to the bitter end, but the days are longer, and the sun has moved a cheering distance to the north, with real warmth on a clear midday. Spirits begin to rise with an accompanying let-down in resistance. Temperatures that would have been greeted as almost balmy in January now are sharp and penetrating; for my mind is ahead of the calendar and only warmth, soft breezes from the south, spongy earth and the first bloodroot can be endured. I am like a slightly dazed boxer with his guard down, defenseless against a blow I have no desire to foresee.

Thus it was in March, 1960, the month that established a long series of brand-new statistics for the weather bureau, records I prefer to forget. One storm piled up seventeen inches of snow, with drifts up to four and five feet. Others preceded it and still others followed. The mercury plummeted to zero and below and anchored there for most of the month. A knifing northwest wind made heavy woolen shirts feel like fishnet. All the snow I had shoveled during the previous three or four months, all the ice I had combatted, all the cold I had survived were brought back and concentrated in March's thirty-one days—all to be battled with a second time. When April finally arrived, cool and wet, I was limp, washed out. May and June were beautiful, for my ends, yet not until July arrived did I feel fully restored to my usual well-being.

Undeniably I am older, now sixty-seven, yet the years are not evident in my physical stamina. Soon after that unforgivable March I was as fit as ever for whatever work was to be done. It is rather that age facilitates a storing up of memories of past tribulations until they become a mental weight of which I am increasingly aware. Previously they could be pressed back, held in abeyance. Last summer, when I was recounting details of my March battle, Mary asked me if I did not dread winters. I denied it emphatically, with unnecessary vehemence, which in itself bespeaks the contrary. Had I agreed, it would have amounted to admitting defeat in advance. To dread something in the future is the last step before surrender. That I could not do. Yet last January, that kind of dread played a considerable role in the big decision that I made in fifteen short minutes.

December opened with snow, and for two months it piled up, layer by layer, following a fixed pattern of fresh snow every few days. By Christmas, manure spreading had been restricted to part of the meadow by the house. I could get that far if I carried only half a load and if I previously had broken tracks with the jeep. Mary went to Washington for the holidays with Scoop and his wife and infant son, and I was glad to be alone as my problems kept me too busy for festivities. The Ford was immobilized, the top of the jeep had been scraped off, leaving it wide open. January brought increasingly bitter winds and more snow at regular intervals. Farmers with big tractors were obliged to stack manure, even on level ground in the valleys, some of them for the first time in their farming lives. I could still reach my small patch in the field if I carried only a third of a load per trip.

The spring also became a matter of concern. There had been almost no rain in October and November, and the snow and cold of December froze the ground so that there was no possibility of seepage to replenish the spring if by chance some thawing did occur. Every other day I floundered down to the springhouse to calculate the diminishing flow. Toward the end of January the flow was so reduced that I knew a water crisis was not far off. On those arctic mornings with the temperature down to fifteen and twenty degrees below zero (in the valleys, thirty below was common) it was quite possible that the spring itself would freeze. Heat from the cows was sucked from the barn by the implacable wind, lowering the temperature there to freezing or a trifle below, and I began to find ice crystals in the drinking cups. Yet the milk went down every morning, manure was spread, and the cows gave no indication of discomfort.

Four more inches of snow fell on January 28, and the outlook was that much bleaker. On the morning of the 29th I went to the barn, shoveled my daily quota of drifted snow to clear the door and went to the milkhouse to prepare for milking. No water from the spigot. I checked the heating cable and it was warm and functioning. I hurried into the barn. No water in the drinking cups, no water from that spigot. Frozen pipe! Somehow, I had not worried about that possibility. The snow appeared to be such an insulating blanket that below-zero weather could hardly penetrate deep into the ground. I was very much in error. So there I was, truly in a jam.

Experience during the past few years simplified the process of sizing up the situation. It was quite mechanical for me to realize what could be done and what could not be done. I might, with great good luck, get the garage man up the hill to thaw the pipe. With a neighbor's tractor hitched on it was a slim possibility, no more. But, *but*, the spring was too low to cope with the constant flow of water through a hose that would have to be maintained to prevent freezing again, for obviously the frost was far down in the ground. There was water in the house but my hapless experiment with hose from house to barn eliminated that as a solution. Hauling water would be a definite gamble against big odds. Three trips a day with nearly a half-ton load either would be entirely beyond the jeep's prowess or would be so hard on it that some vital part would break. Moreover, the cows do not drink as much as they should when water is offered to them in a pail. Some of them, I had learned, flatly refuse it until thirst will not be denied. I had in the past tried giving them water by dumping several cans of it into the concrete feed alley. The result was far from encouraging; the hay and grain got wet and were left untouched. All of which meant the cows would be lacking in body requirements, an unbearable thought, and milk production would quickly fall off. As for the drinking trough at the springhouse, it was buried in several feet of snow and frozen solid.

Appraised from every angle, the situation was desperate. I was in a corner and knew I was licked. The quicker I got rid of the cows, the better, for their sakes more than mine. I finished milking, took the milk down, came back and had breakfast, all automatically while I examined every aspect of the catastrophe, seeking a way out, yet knowing this time it was in vain. At nine o'clock on that wretched Sunday morning I drove down again and almost knocked Richard and Bea off their chairs by announcing I was selling out. In the end, however, when they understood all I was up against, they agreed there was little else to do. So I phoned a local cattle dealer I knew and demanded prompt action. He promised to come the next morning, Monday, if I would meet him at the bottom of the hill to drive him up in the jeep, for my hill road has a reputation in the countryside.

The balance of that Sunday was sheer misery. At times I was totally numb, unable to think; at other intervals, thoughts tumbled over each other, uselessly, hopelessly. I did chores willingly just to keep occupied. I hauled water and felt a weird satisfaction because it was such a hellish job in bitter weather. That helped to silence doubts as to my decision. In the barn I hardly dared look at the cows.

I picked up the dealer the next morning; he inspected the herd and named a price. It was a bit lower than the minimum I had fixed in my mind, but I accepted it. Haggling over a couple of hundred dollars was beyond me. My one concern was to get those cows moved and, upon my insisting, he promised to be back with a truck early that afternoon. An interminable wait it was. No sound of a truck by four o'clock. It would be dark by five. Something, all too evidently, had gone wrong. So I went to the barn to get down hay for the night and was just starting out in the jeep for a load of water when a big tractor, with truck in tow, turned into my lane. The truck had stalled a little above the foot of my hill, then slithered into the ditch. The biggest tractor in the region had been commandeered, and at last they had arrived, prepared to make the two trips that would be necessary. I flatly refused to have anything to do with the loading, staying in the house and downing a couple of huge slugs of whiskey, which merely depressed me below what had seemed to me the very nadir of depression. They departed, they returned, and at nearly ten o'clock they knocked at the door, cold and tired. Glasses were filled with wine. I congratulated them on completing the job; and after bursts of laughter over remarks that I must get cold at night, ought to have a female foot-warmer, one that wore snowshoes, and so forth, they went on their way. For the first time it struck me. It was my birthday. On the day I turned sixty-seven, I had terminated nearly fourteen years of dairying. I drank more wine but not at all as a gesture of celebration.

Three days of torment followed. I could not suppress the constantly recurring accusation that I could have performed all the extra labor demanded, that at least I should have made the effort, that the fates would have relented and shortly restored the ordered routine of other days. Then, for the first time in my farming career, I found solace instead of despair in one of the weather's nastiest fits of temper. Fifteen inches of snow fell, and a ferocious wind piled up drifts of three to four feet. The jeep did not have a chance of moving, and shoveling represented such a gigantic job that ten men could not have opened a passage to the barn, with the wind dumping snow back as fast as it was removed. Had the cows been in the barn I would have been in a panic—all my splendid cows looking to me for water and I utterly helpless to aid them. Not for three days did the township plow succeed in toiling up the hill, spreading great waves of snow to each side like a ship at sea. For three days and nights the cows would have been without water. To think of it, the acute distress in their bellowing, their high expectation every time I opened the door and their harrowing disappointment because I had failed them for reasons beyond their understanding, to think of all that still terrifies me. I could only be vastly pleased, even elated, that I had moved fast and that they were gone to other barns where their placid lives would continue.

10.

Finished. A grim word. And it should be qualified. I was finished as a dairy farmer, and the conviction was already firm that I would not attempt to rebuild a herd, not on my hilltop. Otherwise there was no reason for despair. I took stock of the new situation and found it not at all black, not even gray. I was in excellent health, there was some money in the bank, I owned a house and barn and land clear of all debts, and I was completely free—without a single responsibility other than feeding the cats, that wandered about as befuddled as I was by a barn empty of living creatures. For years I had been trying to get some writing done, seemingly so feasible with the leisure I could command, only to be hampered by the bond with my cows, a relationship so close that I could rarely keep them out of my thoughts. Now that tie was severed and I could substitute for it a chain to a typewriter.

After several weeks the initial shock had shrunk to minute dimensions. No longer do I awaken at four-thirty a.m. with milking on my mind. No longer do I start from my chair at certain hours, still controlled by the old regime and persuaded I should be doing chores. Instead, I am relaxed as I have not been since I came to High Meadows. I deride the weather when it is bad, cruise in the woods on pleasant days. Plans are slowly evolving to make use of the barn, that "noble structure" as Scoop first dubbed it. Still being loyal to my cows, I look about me and find a variety of reasons for being highly optimistic.

One, for instance, is: what better spot could I be in than right here on my hilltop while the world frets and fumes, threatens to explode in a dozen places on almost any given day? Several decades ago I would have been eager to get involved, no matter how minor the role. Not any more. All the present tumult is for younger blood. Two world wars and the intervening years when world peace was just as much a will-o'-the-wisp as it is today, have sufficed to relegate me to the side lines. I follow daily events via the radio but with a sense of total detachment, coupled with near-conviction that there will be scant betterment during my remaining years.

Mankind does not strike me as being greatly advanced from the time the first small tribe of primitives encountered a rival tribe and the first war was fought. Two fundamental motives provoked that initial clash, survival and the desire to dominate. The former is less pertinent at present unless it is understood as the fear of being conquered; the latter is just as pronounced, perhaps more so, than at any other time in man's recorded history of some five thousand years. These motives are evident in every phase of modern life, from the necessity of earning a living to the appetite for money and power that rarely admits satiety. Notwithstanding phenomenal achievements in science, moments of splendor in the arts and in thinking, impressive advances in material well-being, man remains greedy and envious, as he always has been. He wars with his competitors, industries war among themselves, religions are at war with each other, nations vie for supremacy. Can there be an end to it? Not that I can foresee.

The present threat of global conflict has the same genesis as that of the conflicts that have preceded it. Communism is aware that it cannot survive while democracy exists. Since atomic warfare means irreparable devastation for both sides, even if they turn to nuclear bombs only as an ultimate resort, in the manner of Hitler who sought to bring his enemies down in his own inevitable defeat, war will be fought on economic fields. Which side will win that merciless battle is not for me to predict and in one sense it will make little difference. For dissident elements will soon emerge, they will coalesce to increase their power, nuclear bombs will become common property, and the old cycle will be revived. Man does not easily slough off his primitive traits.

Spengler, of course, predicted the decline of the West, that it is already on the downward trend and would soon come to dictatorships, the last stage before oblivion. Well, since he wrote in 1918, we have had Mussolini, Hitler and Stalin, now followed by Khrushchev, a semidictator, Mao Tse-tung and a variety of minor despots. Toynbee places his hope for world order in a Universal Church Militant. Niebuhr relies on a vague Christian faith that will permit man to fulfill himself in eternity. Herbert Muller, a learned and gentle critic, believes the dignity of man will not be denied. Northrop holds for an eventual marriage of Western science and theory with the compassion and equanimity of the Orient. Far be it from me to take exception to the diverse judgments of such scholars. But I can turn to Unamuno and his summons "to live seeing that we all have to die; to live because life is an end in itself," joining it with Camus' belief that "living is the absurdity of life."

Or perhaps all such theorizing will come to naught if a close rein is not soon placed on population growth. According to some dealers in statistics, if the present rate of growth continues for another hundred years or even less, there will not be, speaking very literally, elbow room left. People will be packed together as in a New York subway train at rush hours. The world population will be about ten billion people. At present a world population of some three billion obtains its agricultural foods from three billion acres of cultivated land. These foods are unevenly distributed, with large areas in the Western Hemisphere showing surpluses while the densely populated Orient is undernourished. Yet equal distribution of existing food production would hardly suffice to assure an adequate diet for all the peoples of the world. Approximately 1.3 billion acres of land remain that could be, at great expense, cleared and made suitable for the plow and grazing. It would appear that even the most advanced scientific methods of cultivation, aided by modern machinery, would be strained to the breaking point to provide more than minimum nutritional requirements for a total population over three times that of today. On the other hand, if hunger persists as populations increase, uprisings by great masses of human beings will be inevitable; human tidal waves will break over national boundaries in search of better living conditions. Millions of people facing death by starvation will prefer to risk death by machine guns in the hope that some at least will escape to conditions that cannot be worse than those in which they are trapped and doomed.

It is not for me to be alarmed by such prospects. My years

are in my favor on that score. I do, nevertheless, try occasionally to foresee what awaits my infant grandson who will be forty in the year A.D. 2000 provided atomic warfare does not occur. Society will certainly have to be tightly organized with many, if not all of the personal liberties enjoyed today eliminated. Duties essential to existence will have to be performed under strict regimentation. There will be a ruling or governing class, a huge bureaucracy that will compare with the present middle class, and there will be a vast multitude of workers. Regulations, of necessity, will demand absolute compliance by the people; otherwise the whole intricate machine of government will falter and break down. The popular voice of the democratic state will be stilled or go unheeded; for decisions will be far too vital, bluntly involving life or death, to be entrusted to public vote. And that? All that sounds very much like the present Communist state. If so, I want no part of it.

Some students place their hopes in world government. Ideally, it offers the possibility of Utopia. Practically, it presents problems of such magnitude that expectations of fulfillment clash with a realistic view. Just one phase of it balks imagination. Try to imagine the huge armed force that would be required to police all the nations of the globe to put down revolts and maintain order. Ruthlessness would be the order of the day, and a police state would be the inevitable sequel. Yet would ruthlessness of maximum power be able to keep rigid control over such diverse elements of humanity as Chinese, Indian, Arab, Slav, Latin, African and Anglo-Saxon, bind them into an international unit that would submit to a single governing body? History is made up of failures by one power to inflict submission upon another. Sooner or later rebellion has thrown off the yoke. Then what chance is there of keeping a dozen or more great powers in passive surrender —when man is ever greedy and envious?

Harrison Brown's *The Challenge of Man's Future* deserves wide reading and long meditation. Therein he details facts, figures and solidly based estimates on the world's natural wealth at present, what will become of it in a few decades and what unrestricted population growth portends. It will give any reader pause for thought. If it alarms him, so much the better; for the problems that lie ahead mean all too literally the difference between life and extinction. There is no melodrama in the book, only a clear, cold look at reality. In conclusion, he hopes that the problems can be solved; he believes man is resourceful enough to solve them, but as a realist he is not exactly optimistic.

Enough of such speculation. What will be, will be. Right now it is late March. Most of that thick covering of snow that began to pile up early in December has been eaten away by several days of warm weather, though thick ice still blocks the barn door, always reluctant to depart because of the northern exposure. Not long now and it will be gone, however, and the swallows will arrive to bring a bit of fluttery life to those two rows of empty stanchions, a desolate sight I still avoid.

In the past the birds have returned almost overnight to augment my regular all-winter customers. Bluejays, chickadees, sparrows, in considerable numbers, have had their winter rations of suet; occasionally downy woodpeckers and nuthatches have fought off the strident jays for possession of the lump of fat hanging from a rambler branch outside a living-room window. There I can watch them while eating lunch, the chickadees scattering in brief panic as the jays streak in, the jays giving way with complaining shrieks before the woodpeckers. Just once during the winter a pileated woodpecker moved in for a banquet, sharp black and white against the snow, his red crest brilliant as flame. No bird dared to oppose his stay, for he is almost the size of a crow.

And the crows discovered the suet this year, for the first time. The rose branch is too supple for their weight; and, crafty as always, they launched their attack from the ground. After taking off almost vertically one would spear its beak into the solid fat, then close its wings, hoping that its falling weight would pull the suet free. He seldom succeeded, the branch whipping free after bending close to the ground, but Joe Crow always got at least a mouthful. When I put out the suet I suspend it with baling twine nearly a foot below the branch. The voracious jays cannot balance for long on the chunk and depart with the largest morsel they can snatch. This gives the timid chickadees their innings, until the jays return. For a long time I was puzzled to find the suet and twine wrapped around the branch by repeated turns until the suet was close to the branch, allowing the jays to monopolize the feast. This I did not deem fair, though—so I thought—I admired the jays for being smart enough to keep flipping the fat over the branch until it was short hauled. I never saw them actually doing this, yet it seemed the only explanation. However, they did not deserve my admiration. The crows were responsible, unintentionally. When they pulled the suet down and it flipped back it frequently swung over the branch until all the twine was wrapped up, to the delight of the jays that shrilled their approval.

Crows are fascinating, far more so than any other bird. Tough, brazen, unbelievably canny, they are always good for a laugh. I don't boast about it to neighbor farmers, who curse them and wage unremitting war on them, but I feed my crows daily throughout the winter and even in summer. Every morning one or two plop into a small ash tree by the kitchen. There they perch, one foot above the other on a perpendicular branch, in neat balance, a twig too weak to bear them if it were not straight up and down, and make known their arrival. Pumping back and forth, necks outstretched in defiance of the whole world, they give forth their raucous challenge. They remain in the tree until I have tossed out pieces of stale bread and scraps of meat and returned indoors; then they descend. After years of this they are still wary, sidling awkwardly to a morsel, ready to take off in an instant. In a last-minute hurry each tries to get at least three pieces in its beak. I have watched them pile three bits of bread into a three-decker sandwich that could be grabbed at one time. Then they are off to the meadow to dine at leisure. They eat practically anything, even tainted meat. In fact, crows, abetted by beetles and ants, reduce dead woodchucks to skeletons though the flesh is putrid.

I made one experiment that gives me a laugh every time I think of it. A hard-cooked egg got pushed out of sight in the refrigerator and stayed there unnoticed for a couple of weeks. Not caring to test it as a sample of the kind of eggs the Chinese store for a year or more, I tried it on Joe Crow. I suppose crows rely on vision and hearing, both unusually acute, for on numerous occasions I have gone onto the terrace, scanned every tree in view, also the sky, without noting a trace of a crow; yet a minute after I throw down something edible, at least one crow will come zooming out of nowhere. Anyway, I laid the egg on the ground and retired indoors. Promptly a crow sailed into the ash tree to study that white object. Down he came, examined it more closely, gave it a couple of shoves to make sure it wouldn't explode. At last he opened his beak to its widest and tried to pick up the egg. No luck. It slipped out on every attempt. He was obviously mystified, likewise annoyed. He performed a few mamba steps around it, determined to solve the puzzle. He pecked at it tentatively, made up his mind. He made a quick lunge at the egg and speared it on his closed beak. He paused momentarily, apparently worried because he could not open his beak, then took off. Now an egg is not negligible in weight and when it is at the extreme end of a crow's axis of flight balance it is not to be taken, may I say, lightly. Joe got off the ground only to have his head sag down, steering back to earth. His wings flapped strenuously and he was still air-borne, but down went his head again. With a tremendous effort he barely skimmed the rail fence along the road, lost altitude once more, saw the stone wall ahead and seemed headed for a crash. The Wright brothers were never in more precarious flight than Joe Crow. But he made it, with truly desperate wing action, and survived a one-point landing just beyond the wall. He shook the egg from his beak and attacked it wrathfully as the cause of near disaster. Moreover, he seemed to relish his meal —shell and all, for all I know.

I am not a dedicated bird watcher, wandering through the woods with glasses and a stick for notching each new specimen observed. But birds are diverting to have around; they add color and life to the surroundings. Kildees and robins are the earliest spring arrivals, and the thin cry of the kildee is welcome news that winter is coming to an end. Abruptly, I am aware of the stuttering call of red-winged blackbirds; then a flycatcher appears on the light wires, twitching its tail until a gnat is seen and a quick veering dart captures it. A cardinal flashes brightly in a bare apple tree. A kestrel or sparrow hawk, hardly larger than a blue jay, perches on the light pole of an evening before sailing off to the woods for the night, and the handsome marsh hawks float overhead, brown and white against blue sky. Vainly I hope to see one plummet to a field to snatch a field mouse, though I once did spot one carrying a snake that must have measured eighteen inches.

There is nothing here remindful of Capistrano, but the swallows are as regular in their arrival. April 25 is the usual date for the first pair to appear, inspect the barn and then, I presume, pass the good word to their pals; for the following day, a dozen or more will entrance me by their joyous, effortless flight in and out of the barn, around it, high, high in the air and then swiftly down till wingtips touch the ground. They are friendly residents of the barn where I watch them while milking, *could* watch them, I must get used to saying, for milking is in the past tense henceforth. Usually they take over the nests of last year, adding their own blobs of mud to match them to their personal tastes, just as the housewife does when the family moves into a new dwelling. If there is nothing for rent, or what is available is not to the liking of the new tenants, they build new nests, an intriguing construction job requiring tireless trips to mud patch and back to the selected corner near the barn ceiling, where the overhanging nest gradually takes form.

Soon afterward I shall watch for that ever-recurring instinct at work, instinct that surely traces back through countless generations. Eggs are laid and hatched, and shortly thereafter five absurdly wide yellow beaks line up on the rim of the nest. Before the eyes are open the infants sense the arrival of Pa or Ma, and all five beaks gape open expectantly. The parent swallows keep good track of which was the last one to receive an insect, each baby getting fed in turn. So they all grow fast, the five packed close together. I assume that up to this time all food has gone into growth with nothing remaining to be eliminated. Now nature's call must be answered. At the same time, the long established and deeply implanted rule must be observed—don't foul your own nest. Suddenly great movement takes place in the nest. One fledgling elbows to right and left, the others are shoved to each side, until it can squirm around in reverse position, head inside, tail over the rim. Duty done, instinct followed, the commotion is repeated and amid squeaks of protest from the others, the good little child is back in position, beak ready for another meal. How long ago, I would like to know, did that first act of sanitation in the home take place?

Nature at work, ceaselessly experimenting, succeeding here and there, failing as often as not, evolving monsters as well as weird midgets, many defenseless yet surviving if only by virtue of sheer numbers, a few of which will escape the enemy host. . . . Look at the praying mantis, helpless against attack except—and nature always provides some kind of exception. The mantis can vanish as you look at it, crouching along a twig until it is indistinguishable from the twig itself.

The other evening at dusk I went to the terrace to bring in the cat dish and found a 'possum cleaning up some crumbs. Last summer a 'possum was a nightly raider of the strawberry patch, identifiable by the manner in which it wallows over the plants instead of picking its way as a 'coon or a woodchuck would. I tried to trap it and several times found the trap sprung but no other sign of the marauder. I vowed revenge, for it was exasperating day after day to find a quantity of plump ripe berries half eaten or crushed, though I knew it would not be easy to spot a 'possum, which is a nocturnal animal. Therefore, when this one appeared on the terrace I got the gun at once. It waddled away a few yards when I came out the door; otherwise it paid no attention to me. It is not a beguiling beast, which may be a form of protection, for I noticed Snazzy, the cat, evinced no desire to make a meal of it, as she would a squirrel. Nevertheless, vulnerable as the 'possum is, it has survived for eons and apparently will continue to do so. Not this one, however, for I shot it—and then wondered at nature's almost implausible pattern of reproduction for the 'possum.

The 'possum is a marsupial—like the kangaroo it carries its young in a pouch until they are weaned. Once in the pouch, they are secure—but consider the hazard following birth. As many as fifty young emerge, each about half an inch long. With no help from the mother, each blind and feeble offspring must make its way along the mother's belly to the pouch. However, in that pouch there are only eleven nipples to which the young can fasten for nourishment and warmth. Instead of simplifying the method so that only eleven young are born, with immediate access to the pouch, nature prefers complications, sure that out of some fifty the requisite eleven will reach the waiting haven. All the others, of course, must die. What prodigality with life! And thus there are plenty of 'possums in the world, defenseless though they may appear to be.

April will soon arrive and I shall be busy in the garden, loosening earth beneath the old, decayed mulch so that early peas can be sown and seedbeds for flowers will be ready when the last frost has whitened the ground. The catbirds will install themselves in the tangle of grape and hop vines along the stone wall, and I shall talk to them for they like that and will sing and chatter in response as long as I continue. And I shall remind myself frequently that this coming summer I shall not have to worry about the cows invading that private preserve, which they managed to do once or twice a year. They soon learned that one bar in the fence by the house was usually loose so that I could remove it when the jeep was needed to haul bales of old hay or whatever. Skipper, daughter of Bebop and a replica in every way in temperament and appearance, was specially adept at tossing the bar aside with her head and prancing through, followed by all the others. Not that there was exceptional grazing in the garden, and they did not really crave the pea vines or lettuce they would snatch at on the run. It was just that they knew they were not supposed to be in the garden and to outwit me was a glorious game. They were more than pleased just to romp about, tails high, plunging and bucking and racing while I tried to get behind them and herd the whole outfit back through the gate. They would stop to watch me as I circled them and at the last moment all break past me, blatting their elation, delighted to hear me yell at them.

No, they will not pester me next summer or other summers thereafter; but on more than one occasion I shall realize how greatly I miss them, admitting I would vastly prefer to have them, trying me to the limit of temper yet so absurdly childish in their capers that I invariably wound up laughing. From now on the farm is haunted; there are bovine phantoms awaiting me wherever I go.

Every meadow has its favorite spots where I could pretty well count on finding Bebop and Lollypop; and once they were discovered in the opaque light of dawn I could be sure the others were in the vicinity. Toots, Gaby and Skipper would be together, for they were inseparable since they were calves all the same age. Daffy, Granny and Dido likewise would be close to each other, for they also had grown up together, a year younger than the first trio. Sheba and Bori, always less gregarious and likely to be farther away, could be counted on to come ambling through the gloom as soon as the others got to their feet and we all started for the barn. And Duchess and Nike, the youngest, might dally to the last moment; then, afraid of being left behind, come along in such a rush that I would have to step out of their path while they charged by.

Memories left by such close friends will never fade. I knew every one of them intimately, each one's idiosyncrasies, likes and dislikes, and they knew me. They understood when I got in a rage, for there was good cause—unwarranted stubbornness by one or two to comply with the usual discipline. The delinquents were aware that they were guilty and deserved the solid whack they received. For we all accepted a kind of code of manners which could be transgressed out of sheer mischief or prankishness and the culprit forgiven, whereas unreasonable perverseness was unpermissible. I was obliged to recognize these differentiations, and frequently they were of so fine a nature that it was difficult to be sure whether punishment was merited. For a cow's disposition can be ruined by punishment for which she can understand no cause. Windy provided a good example of this failure to follow the code of good behavior for no good reason apparent to me, yet punishment was not deserved as I eventually discovered. She was an unusually docile creature, not at all high strung or given to tantrums of any kind, friendly though not asking for affection, a big slow animal that I relied upon to follow the rules. I became certain that she was one who would always be in her place, ready for established procedure, in and out of the barn. One evening I brought the herd in for milking and as each stepped onto the platform I locked it into the stanchion. There was the customary one or two who preferred to roam about or indulge in a last-minute butting game, a mild flurry which was quickly straightened out, for the cows were always eager for their ration of grain. Taking a final glance down the line, I noted that Windy's stanchion was empty. I looked out the door and Windy stood there.

I ordered her inside, but she didn't move. I rubbed her nose and gave her a push. She resisted. I slapped her flank and shoved some more until she was half through the door, when she turned and jumped away. I was slightly annoyed for I wanted to get on with milking; but after a few more futile tries, always ending with that burst for freedom, I decided she would get over whatever antipathy had seized her and would enter her stanchion. Nevertheless, when I had finished milking the other cows, there she was, still a few steps from the door, watching me but showing no inclination to enter. I tried coaxing her, I tried switching her, shoving her, swearing at her, all to no avail. She was determined not to go into the barn. I noosed a rope around her horns and attempted to drag her in, but every time I got her head in the door she would suddenly leap back—I was being hauled, not she.

Coping single-handed with a refractory cow is not easy. It is impossible to remain behind her if she is determined to shy off to an unguarded side. Yet she had to be milked. I slammed the door shut and sat down inside to smoke a cigarette while I considered the silly predicament. I was in a temper, yet there was something so odd about Windy's obstinacy that I checked an urge to take a club and really sock her a few blows. I opened the door and pleaded with her, cajoled her, smacked her, to no purpose whatsoever. She simply would not budge. By now it was quite dark and the other cows were restless, wanting to be turned out. I closed the door, drove below in the jeep. I needed assistance.

Two neighbors were enlisted, and we hurried back. Windy was right where I had left her, not wishing to stray any more then she wanted to come inside. Since she was solid black, all I could see of her in the dark was two glowing green-and-blue orbs. With three of us to close in on her we managed to steer her, inch by inch, through the door, which I promptly closed. Windy regarded her mates, all in stanchions. She stood before her stanchion, eying her grain in the feed alley, but sniffing suspiciously at an unaccustomed odor that alarmed her. Then I understood what it was. The barn had been whitewashed that morning. Her stanchion was not only very white; it and the platform smelled of damp lime, not an offensive smell but so new and different that Windy wanted none of it. However, after a few minutes, she accepted it as not menacing. I milked her and sent the herd off for the night. How wrong I should have been had I tried to club her into obedience!

Dumpling was another cow that showed me that restraint was the best course until I was absolutely sure of my judgment. She was a Bebop daughter, much larger than her dam but quite similar in character, gentle and easy-going. She was stanchioned next to Bebop, and I was between the two when I milked them. For a time the milking line-up was such that Dumpling was last, and the only one. I took advantage of this to squat on a stool during the process, talking to Dumpling and Bebop alike. Bebop, the long-standing pet of the herd and as desirous of affection as a kitten, got the habit of twisting her head toward me so that I could scratch her nose or let her lick my hand. After a few days of this Dumpling became fidgety while the milking machine was extracting her milk.

Examination showed that it was functioning properly, and I began to speak sternly to her to keep her quiet. She continued to display annoyance or nervousness, and I turned to my elimination gambit, checking over a variety of possible causes. Thus engaged I forgot about Bebop, devoting my time to calming Dumpling. She responded at once, settled down to her usual tractable self. So, with nothing else to do, I returned to playing with Bebop. And that was what bothered Dumpling. A plain case of jealousy. While I was milking her, she as much as informed me, she deserved my full attention. I agreed with her, despite Bebop's evident disappointment, and the difficulty ended.

The incident is amusing, yet indicative of the sensitivity of cows, especially when they are treated as pets, perhaps even spoiled with affection. The urbanite may well look at a cow as a hulking, placid animal, almost witless and totally lacking in nerves. He is far from right. Big, awkward in a curiously graceful way, staid, she is all of those. In addition she is surprisingly intelligent; and unless properly handled, with patience and sympathy, she becomes a bundle of nerves, distrustful of humankind and quick to display her lack of faith with a swift kick in response to a suspect move.

Almost from the beginning I made up my mind that I would not tolerate an undependable cow given to kicking. On my part, it was a combination of fear and resentment, for I was scared of a couple of cows in the original herd that were confirmed kickers when being milked, and resented the fact that they would not respond to kindness. Once ingrained, the kicking habit cannot be overcome, and the anticipation of a foot launched with lethal intent is more than I care to struggle with. Those two recalcitrants were soon disposed of, but throughout the early years when I was obliged to buy cows to build up the herd, I brought home animals that for the most part were unreliable. Not until I had enough heifer calves of my own to raise did I achieve a herd of gentle bovines with confidence in me. Even so, there was one exception; and I still wonder what went wrong, where the fault lay, whether one meets an occasional throwback to the wild state that rejects every effort toward domestication. Certainly there are atavistic traits in humans.

Duchess was out of Gaby, a splendid animal in every way, and I was elated to have her first heifer calf. From the start the calf received every attention, we came to know each other intimately and she responded generously, asking for affection and returning it. She was handsome, more white than black, with that same air of royalty that Gaby possessed and the lines of a fine purebred. I congratulated myself frequently on owning such a promising addition to the herd. She grew up and was bred, and I was agog for the time she would become a milker, possibly with a heifer calf of her own.

I followed what had become regular practice with my heifers during the last two months before calving. Every two or three days I would gently massage Duchess's expanding udder and finger the four teats to familiarize her with my touch, so that the next step of attaching the milking machine would not be too abrupt. Taking time for this pays off later, and I have had a few heifers that accepted the machine without the slightest show of resentment. As a rule, however, they do object for a day or two before they become accustomed to the big shiny object slung beneath them and tugging firmly to keep the milk flowing. I do not mind if occasionally a foot lashes out in an attempt to knock the machine clear; and while I talk to them, I am usually prepared to note the warning that comes when they shift weight slightly to the off leg, leaving the other leg free for kicking. Patience pays off and soon they forget their disapproval; they let down their milk without hesitation and pay more attention to the grain in front of them than to me and the machine.

Everything proceeded normally with Duchess, with no resentment or nervousness when I stroked her udder. The day came when the pelvic bones at the base of the tail began to spread and I put her in the maternity pen. She calved without great difficulty, a bull, and I fetched warm water for her to drink, forked in a lot of fresh bedding and hung over the rail to pay her lavish compliments. A few hours later the calf was on its feet and nuzzling for a meal. Then trouble started. Duchess would have none of it. Every time her offspring nosed onto her udder, she kicked it aside. She even turned on it and sent it sprawling with a solid butt of her head. As she had horns that could inflict real damage, I watched a little more of this performance, then pushed her out of the pen and escorted her to her stanchion. Thereupon I received the same treatment as the calf. Every attempt to touch her udder, which was distended as to be expected but not so abnormally as to be painful, she froze rigid, began to tremble—and up came that foot, fast and mean.

I spent perhaps fifteen minutes trying to calm her with quiet words, petting her, anything that might soothe her. Still no success. I left her. A cow's udder immediately after freshening is firm because of the milk it contains and a general swelling of all the tissues. Sometimes it is extremely hard, like wood, as a result of "caking," and it may not regain its pliable, spongy condition for a couple of weeks. Soreness of the teats may result, making the milking operation painful. Duchess, however, was not yet at this stage. Nevertheless, if the calf did not suck milk and lessen tension and I could not milk her, either by hand or machine, the congestion would increase and the problem would become serious.

Some time later I returned her to the pen, then watched the calf get the same treatment as before. Again Duchess was put in stanchion. I brought the machine, let her inspect it and smell it, and tried to hook it on. No sooner did she feel one inflation contracting than she exploded, rear end in the air, the machine kicked off the surcingle. She was frantic. I talked to her and tried again. The reaction was even wilder, as though she had been stung by a thousand bees. Well, during the next thirty-six hours, I returned to the fray at intervals, between which she ate and acted quite normal, but the slightest contact with her udder sent her into a thrashing, vicious fit.

There was nothing more I could do—I acknowledged defeat and sold her. I believe the dealer suspected what was wrong. He didn't seem convinced by my lame reason for selling her that the cows were getting too crowded. Anyway, he took her and her calf and I have never inquired since as to what happened. But that interrogation mark lingers. Was I at fault somehow during that pre-natal period and so lost what might have been the best cow in the barn? It is a nagging thought.

Cows have long memories for past errors in judgment and, happily, for kindness. Once a bond of confidence is established they are easy to manage, in and out of the barn. Not for several years have I been bothered by cows breaking through fences and invading a neighbor's field. Since my fences are, I confess, rather sketchy and there are places where they could step over a low wire with ease, yet they never do, the one explanation is that they were quite content to stay at home. My carelessness, my failure to maintain upright posts and taut barbed wire, has brought moans of anguish from my neighbor Richard who wants to rent about fifty acres of woods, brook and North Meadow for his young stock. His heifers are inclined to break out wherever they can worry a post and wire to the ground and as lessee the responsibility is his to keep them within bounds. That means a good mile of fence to be repaired and renewed—while I sit back with no cows to worry about, not always pleased with my enforced release from bovine bothers.

Whatever my woes at any given moment, I could always forget them by sitting on a bale of hay and watching the long line of heads chewing down wads of hay while gazing raptly into space, an atmosphere of serenity that dissipated tension as when the first fingers of sunlight slip over the horizon and stir damp fog into streamers that drift apart and vanish. That was the way I discovered a neat trick performed by some of the cows that persuaded me that they are capable of logical thought, of reasoning a problem to its conclusion.

These cows did not like the noisy gushing of water when they pressed down the paddle in their drinking cups. It interfered with their drinking. The paddle operates on a hinge and can be lifted up to permit cleaning the cup. With a little figuring they came to the solution. First they pressed down on the paddle until the bowl was filled. Then they coiled their tongues around the paddle and triumphantly lifted it until it stood erect. And with eyes half-closed in complacent satisfaction they drank the bowl dry. When thirst returned, a nudge of the chin flipped the paddle back in place so that more water could be drawn. To my mind that is proof of reasoning powers, of analyzing the several steps required and evolving them into a sequence that produced the result they desired.

Intelligence is obvious in another trick they play. When a cow is dry, not giving milk during the two months or so before calving, she does not get a grain ration. But if the cow in the adjoining stanchion is milking and receives grain, temptation is overwhelming to filch some of that desirable mixture. Down she goes on her knees for greater neck stretching, and that coil of tongue encircles a mouthful of grain and brings it within reach as effectively as any elephant with its long trunk could do. The victimized cow resents such outright theft and tries to butt the poacher away. So the poacher gets crafty. She waits till her neighbor has stuffed her mouth with grain, then makes a menacing move. The neighbor responds with a quick swing of the head and in the doing loses half the mouthful, scattering it toward the interloper—who smugly laps it up and gets set for a repeat performance. How can one help being amused by such shenanigans?

Perhaps there is also a sense of humor in some of their antics. On pasture one will butt and shove another until the latter is roused to vengeance and turns wrathfully on her tormentor. And that is precisely what is desired. Away dashes the offender, the other in hot pursuit. Then the whole herd gets mildly hysterical and the game begins. Up and down the meadow they go at full gallop, tails stiff as rods, heads bobbing in simulation of ferocious attack. The one who started it all is in the lead, enjoying the romp to its limit, and I can almost hear her laughing amid the silly blatting of her pals. What a huge joke!

They delighted in plaguing me by stealing my gloves from my hip pocket, by snatching my cap when I had to work close to them and tossing it as far off as they could. And they were especially delighted to get a mouthful of my shirt and hang on till I was half-naked—all the more so if they finally pestered me into swearing at them. There they would stand, legs apart, mocking me in the hope I would chase them, like so many kids trying to get "shag."

Among the twelve or so cows I had at one time, personalities were sharply defined and I learned to deal with each one as an individual. This was more noticeable when I had raised every member of the herd and had lived closely with them from birth. Bella was the last of the original herd to depart. She was all black except for four white socks, big, stolid, rather stupid, I thought in the beginning. But she was not stupid. Rather, she simply accepted her role as milk maker and asked in return only food and shelter. She gave the impression of dullness, of a lacking of spirit, simply because she was so steady, so thoroughly reliable. She did not actually resent affection but she never invited it. Petting her brought no more response than fondling a big boulder. Not for some time did I appreciate how welcome it was to have a cow that did not show the sparkle of a Gaby, yet was absolutely dependable. Spirit and dependability make an ideal combination but, if forced to choose between the two, I prefer the latter.

Six generations stemmed from Bella: Noella, Windy, Bori, Daffy, Nike and Corky, the latter only six months old when the herd departed. This was the longest string of descendants I had from any of my cows. It was interesting to watch the change in successive generations from Bella's indifference to affection. She, of course, was too old and set in her ways to alter in the few years I owned her. Windy was a black carbon copy of Bella in appearance and character, and perhaps I was deluding myself when I thought she was slightly more responsive. With Bori, however, there was no mistaking an improvement. Sometimes she would shake off my hand when I scratched her ear, but as a rule she accepted it and indicated a liking for it. With Daffy the transformation was almost complete, and Nike contributed the final touch. In fact, she became, at two years, a pest as well as a pet, for at milking time she insisted on getting her head around where I could rub her nose or she could chew my wrist while the machine did its job. And Corky, I am convinced, would have rivaled Nike by the time she had her first calf.

So a point was scored by the environmental school. Inheritance, however, was dominant in the transmission of other traits. Every one of Bella's progeny displayed the same steadiness; and though they would follow if the others started trooping through a hole in the fence, I doubt if they ever opened the hole even in their ebullient youth. Bella had to be disposed of when she was sixteen years old and had been one of the two best milkers in the group that came with the farm. Artificial breeding proved its worth as each descendant matured and poured more milk into the pail. Bori was at her peak of six years when my dairying ended, and she could be counted on for better than 12,000 pounds of milk during one lactation. At the end of ten months I had difficulty halting her flow of milk to allow her two months of rest before the next calving. Both Daffy and Nike gave every promise of doing better. What cause could there be for such regular improvement other than artificial insemination and the top-flight bulls a co-operative made available, bulls valued at $20,000 or more? So Bella and her daughters figured prominently in the herd from start to finish.

Grandma Nellie was Bella's rival in the old herd. She was an amazing old girl, youthful to the end, friendly and easy to handle. Her line, however, did not show milking progress with the same regularity as Bella's which demonstrates that artificial breeding or any other factor is never infallible. Blondy was not the equal of Nellie, nor was her daughter Vicky. Not until Lollypop entered the production line did a marked improvement become apparent. Her udder was better formed, her body was larger and better proportioned. In addition she was even-tempered and loved to be fondled. As a calf she responded by trying to get a whole hand in her mouth to suck and chew, hence her name.

Bad luck interrupted her milking career. Either she or her neighbor cow stepped on not one but two teats at the same time, mangling them into bloody stubs. This is probably the most common accident in every dairy barn. During the last years I succeeded in controlling it by leaving vacant stanchions between every two cows to eliminate crowding, but it was not entirely effective. Even in barns equipped with stall rails separating the cows, such accidents will occur. And there is nothing more exasperating than to approach a cow for milking and find a teat swollen and maimed by a clumsy hoof. Days of doctoring are required; the teat is too sore to permit using the machine so that milk must be extracted by inserting a slender hollow tube into the teat beyond the sphincter muscle and slowly massaging the milk into a pail, with Bossie on edge and prepared to kick in protest, sometimes dislodging the tube into the bedding. The proverbial needle in a haystack is closely rivaled by a milking tube in straw bedding. Lolly was way off in milk for two lactations and never got over her nervousness at milking time.

Meanwhile she presented me with a handsome daughter, Granny, in honor of Grandma Nellie. Whoever acquired Granny after I sold the herd became owner of as promising a three-year-old as one could wish for. Mostly white and as big as her dam, she was a sweet animal, as easy to work with as Bella's offspring. When she dropped her first calf, she started right in making sixty pounds of milk a day. She accepted the machine without a quiver on the first try and never lifted a foot for any reason. Yet she was full of spirit, playful as a puppy, with two ruined sweatshirts to her credit, resulting from a game of you-push-me we used to engage in and during which her horn caught in the shirt, to her delight but not to mine.

Only two other breeding lines were followed during the last years: the lovely Gaby and the clownish Toots were the progenitors. They are both examples of the uncertainty of breeding. Gaby had all the lines of a purebred, big, finely proportioned, with a good udder and, though not a high producer, capable of better than 10,000 pounds of milk—all in all, a specimen whose daughters could be counted on for improvement. Yet not one has even equalled Gaby; two fell woefully short and were sold. Gaby II was a four-year-old last year and was doing fairly well; she might have rivaled her Ma in her prime this year though my hopes were not too high. Sheba, her older sister, barely rated good in my opinion. The youngest, Duchess, had not yet calved. And there was her forerunner, the first Duchess, who was such a disappointment. I had just about decided to abandon the line.

Toots was as harum-scarum in her offspring as she was in her general deportment. She was a good producer but her udder soon weakened, becoming so pendulous that milking was difficult and the teats were repeatedly gashed by brambles or barbed wire which she persisted in climbing through. So she was sold rather early, leaving two daughters, the exceptional Bebop and the promising Pixie. The latter's udder, however, soon showed the same weakness of structure as Toots'; and a couple of years ago when her milk dropped close to zero only three months after calving, for cause completely unknown to me, I disposed of her. Curiously enough, her daughter, Toots, did the same thing as a four-year-old and I

181

had so little confidence that she might make a come-back that I sold her.

Ah, but such disheartening events can be forgotten, even forgiven, because old Toots gave me Bebop, a cow I shall never forget. She was born in 1949, so that we were together for almost my entire career as a dairyman and she was elder statescow at the end. Bebop was as close to the ideal cow as I would ever expect to own. She possessed a wealth of spirit that was displayed in playfulness and good-natured fun, not in excitability. She was of the *gamine* type, ever ready to try my patience but terminating her game in time to oblige me to laugh at her instead of scold. I vow I found her with a grin on her big muzzle when she zoomed into the barn, scattering her mates, creating mild bedlam, only to come to a sliding halt at her stanchion and enter it with innocent decorum. Or when she eluded me and skipped into the feed alley for no reason other than to pester me. For the feed alley is too narrow for a cow to turn around in, and it was up to me to coax her to back up, which she would do so meekly and obediently that I could do no more than tweak her ear in reprisal.

With all her high jinks she was thoroughly reliable at milk-ing time, standing stock still while the machine was attached. In addition she made a lot of milk. In her prime of six years and for four more years she poured out a can of milk a day, ten gallons, for the first two or three months of her lactation period, making a total for ten months of about 17,000 pounds, a first-class performance that only top-flight purebreds surpass.

It was this exceptional capacity for milk making, plus her age of eleven years, that caused her attack of milk fever when she calved year before last. Milk fever results from a deficiency of calcium in the cow's system. Her udder bulged with milk just before the calf was born, the milk drained off her natural reserve of calcium, and she was too weak to get onto her feet. More troubling were her lackluster eyes, as though all will to resist was gone. I summoned the vet for emergency treatment, and he gave her intravenous doses of calcium and dextrose, admitting that he was worried about her appearance. But I had no intention of allowing her to lapse into complete surrender. I sat with her, talked endlessly, told her she must recover— I know she listened by the way she flicked an ear and looked at me with dull eyes.

Gradually she regained some strength. The vet treated her again, and I fed her all the molasses she would eat to provide additional dextrose. When I managed to get her up I took her to her stanchion, propping her up as her rubbery legs gave way momentarily. There I milked out just enough for the calf but no more because I did not want any of her depleted strength to go into making milk. And I continued to talk to her, taking her head in my arms as I had done so often before to show my affection for her, whispering that she was on the mend and that she would be as spry as ever if she would keep on fighting. She did and after a week I could turn her out.

Then she got an infection in her foot, a bruise or cut between her two toes, that became too painful for her to walk. I tried three different vets for treatment, but a variety of salves and ointments failed to bring noticeable improvement. I did become expert at bandaging the foot though that was mainly because Bebop had confidence in me, knew I was trying to help her, and would stand immovable on three feet while I held the injured member between my legs, like a blacksmith shoeing a horse, and wrapped cloth strips into place. Disgusted with the medicaments I had been using, I turned to a homeo-pathic salve we keep in the house for cuts and abrasions. It is made from oil of calendula and has been remarkably effective in the family. It proved equally so with Bebop and once again she could be turned out on pasture.

Some of her spark had been diminished by the long siege, and she was more of a quiet old lady than the frisky matron of a few months before. Inevitably her milk production had been reduced almost to zero, yet she regained a good share of that ability and I was surprised that she could make as much as forty pounds daily. Persistent weakness was also revealed by repeated failure to get her bred. Try as I might, I could not evade the fact that Bebop was approaching her end as a producing member of the herd. I was somewhat consoled by having her daughter, Skipper, a four-year-old spit 'n image of her Ma that gave every promise of equalling her as a milk-maker —but far from enough to permit me to accept parting with a cow to which I had become as completely attached as is humanly possible.

I still cannot say with finality what I would have done if the disastrous events of January had not forced me to dispose of the entire herd. I definitely considered keeping her until old age claimed her. However, if all my cows had to go, then it was a bit easier to include Bebop among them. The gods had made the decision, not me. The cows would all be better off in some other barn. And I would be alone, except for vivid memories.

Not for anything in the world would I have missed those years with the cows. Not only did I get to know them intimately and find them deserving of all the affection I could heap upon them. They taught me many things in return—patience, self-control, appreciation of their rights even when in conflict with my own, a deep understanding of other individuals. There is an ancient Chinese counsel extant centuries before the Christian era: "Do not unto others what you would not have others do unto you." It has profound meaning. Somehow it applies to cows as well as mankind.

What do I do now? Will some new career, vocation, avocation, with its accompanying rosy dream, rise on the horizon and stir me into action? Throughout these past years I have schemed to provide myself with all possible leisure. Without neglecting the cows in the slightest, actually I enjoyed the chores they made necessary. I refined those tasks down to the ultimate minute of efficiency. I boasted of reducing essential labor to three hours a day in summer and about four hours in winter. It was a game that brought me as much spare time as I could fill to some profitable end. Hundreds of books I had long wanted to read or reread have come to the house to occupy bookshelves that I keep building in room after room. Right now books are stacked on tables and bureaus and I must install shelves below the two big living-room windows, one on each side of the fireplace. The local library has received a dozen or so large boxes of books we no longer cared to keep. Even mystery yarns and thrillers find a destination, for I have yet to meet a book so hopelessly awful that I can bring myself to burning it.

Now there are no chores demanding my time and muscle. When I am alone I admit to negligence as to the niceties of housekeeping. I horrify my meticulous neighbor by expounding my theory that lint and dust eventually gather in a few heaps and can be disposed of in a couple of minutes. Otherwise, while I am indoors, books are my major interest, along with what good music I can obtain by radio—and a regrettably, pathetically small portion it is, with disk jockeys and commercials monopolizing the air waves. Yet I do not care to read for more than three hours at a stretch. I tend to get restless; concentration begins to falter. The desire to move about, if only to take a walk, becomes pronounced. Since the cows departed I have felt a definite need for exercise, a physical workout.

I shall allot more time to gardening and give it closer attention. I shall grow more flowers this year—two perennial beds will be started and goaded to a mass of color. But my system of mulching eliminates so much digging, hoeing and raking that extra hours in the garden apparently will be largely devoted to oratory, exhortations and pleadings for faster growth, more buds, sturdier stalks. I have heard that prayer has been resorted to with noticeable results when seedlings receiving devout attention were compared with those condemned to limbo, deprived of pleas to the heavenly host, hence left in the clutch of Satan. However, I am not much good at prayer.

Out my window I count a big barn, thirty by eighty feet, two solid chicken houses and a large shed with a second floor. They look at me accusingly, prodding me to find occupants, animate tenants that squawk or growl or yap or shriek, anything that means life. And I both understand and agree. Chickens get a firm negative vote, I insist to myself. They have no appeal for me. On the other hand, a dozen or so would be easy to care for, and in return I should have eggs and meat.

Geese, by contrast, have great appeal. I delight in their dignity, their belligerence when disturbed. They do not scatter in fluttery panic when someone approaches. Instead they stand their ground, hiss ominously at the intruder, then finally stalk away, without haste, with lordly bearing and feathers ruffling in contempt. Guinea fowl likewise receive my approval. Still half-wild, they are pretty much on their own, roosting in trees, nesting in hedges and giving a raucous reception to strangers. They would provide color and animation. Moreover, roast guinea hen is mighty good eating. As for roast goose, little need be said as to its succulent flesh.

The two chickenhouses and the shed would more than accommodate such new residents. That leaves the barn, in particular the long cow stable, with its many windows and closely fitting doors. So I am considering pigeons, the large meat type. They would have ample room for flying, and nesting boxes could be installed above the stanchions beyond the reach of Snazzy if she should manage to invade the place in quest of young pigeon. What is more delectable than squab slowly braised in a casserole with butter and a little white wine? The stable is roomy enough for some fifty birds without crowding. A flock of that size would have commercial possibilities, for squab find a ready market in the city.

Profit, however, would not be an immediate concern in such plans. Primarily I want more life and color about the place. High Meadows is a farm, after all, and the farm atmosphere must be maintained. If not, it will soon acquire an abandoned air, mournful, with only the house as a breathing, pulsing unit. That I intend to avoid for I have no vestige of thought of leaving the farm. Second, I would have living things to care for, to occupy me daily, no matter how short the time involved. That makes for variety, which I welcome. Third, the menu would benefit by an occasional dish otherwise unobtainable, especially guinea hen and squab.

I know a neighbor who owns a herd of cows, drives a trailer

truck delivering flagstone as far as New York, hires out with his bulldozer for various jobs. Heaven knows how he finds time for all his undertakings. But in addition he insists on having an assortment of feathered diversion: bantams and fancy breeds for showing at local fairs, geese, ducks, plain and fancy, peacocks and hens, turkeys and a few fancy pigeons. They are all pretty much on their own, free to roam and fend for themselves. But they appear to be healthy and certainly they multiply—to the point of utter confusion when they are all startled at the same time and the racket is deafening, a cacophonic chorus so absurd as to force me to join in with loud laughter. I have no intention of arriving at similar chaos in the barnyard, yet I envy him such lively surroundings.

Of one thing I am certain. Turning from udders and horns to feathers and wings should remove the risk of emotional involvement. Parting with the cows was an ordeal I have no wish to repeat. Escorting a brace of geese to market would scarcely stir a ripple to disturb my tranquillity.

So I feel this long venture in rusticity has paid off in full measure. My aim was to secure leisure and calm. They are mine, in quantity, for the years ahead. All the battles with the elements are over. My worries are ended. My only debt is an enormous one and it is owed to the cows. They were the foundation; then, over the years, the buttresses that sustained the entire undertaking, staunch friends when the outlook was at its darkest. Perhaps they had an inkling that one of the coldest winters on record was required to separate us, understood that it was not at all my wish. I shall miss, over and over again, their decorative contribution to my landscape, their sleek black and white against rich green. But I shall welcome their phantoms as I encounter them in every lane, on twisting trails, moving placidly across fields. I may even learn to embrace a wraith.

High Meadows
Pennsylvania
Spring, 1961